SHORTCUTS

130 ALMOST-FROM-SCRATCH RECIPES

ABOUT WEIGHT WATCHERS

Weight Watchers International, Inc. is the world's leading provider of weight management services, operating globally through a network of Company-owned and franchise operations. Weight Watchers holds over 48,000 weekly meetings, where members receive group support and education about healthful eating patterns, behavior modification, and physical activity. Weight-loss and weight-management results vary by individual. We recommend that you attend Weight Watchers meetings to benefit from the supportive environment you'll find there and follow the comprehensive Weight Watchers program, which includes food plans, an activity plan, and a thinking-skills plan. In addition, Weight Watchers offers a wide range of products, publications and programs for those interested in weight loss and weight control. For the Weight Watchers meeting nearest you, call **800-651-6000**. For information on bringing Weight Watchers to your workplace, call **800-8AT-WORK**. Also, visit us at our Web site, **WeightWatchers.com**, or look for *Weight Watchers Magazine* at your newsstand or in your meeting room.

CHICKEN WITH ANDOUILLE
AND PEPPERS, PAGE 76

WEIGHT WATCHERS PUBLISHING GROUP

EDITORIAL DIRECTOR	NANCY GAGLIARDI
CREATIVE DIRECTOR	ED MELNITSKY
PRODUCTION MANAGER	ALAN BIEDERMAN
OFFICE MANAGER AND PUBLISHING ASSISTANT	JENNY LABOY-BRACE
FOOD EDITOR	EILEEN RUNYAN
EDITOR	CAROL PRAGER
NUTRITION CONSULTANT	U. BEATE KRINKE
RECIPE DEVELOPERS	MAUREEN LUCHEJKO, FRANK P. MELODIA, DAVID BONOM, PAUL PICCUITO, JILL SILVERMAN HOUGH
PHOTOGRAPHER	DASHA WRIGHT
FOOD STYLIST	MICHAEL PEDERSON
PROP STYLIST	DEBRAH E. DONAHUE
ART DIRECTOR	LISA CUMMINGS
DESIGNER	DANIELA HRITCU

ON THE COVER: Cheesy Sloppy Joes (***POINTS***® value: **4**), page 158

ABOUT OUR RECIPES

We make every effort to ensure that you will have success with our recipes. For best results and for nutritional accuracy, please keep the following guidelines in mind:

- Recipes in this book have been developed for Weight Watchers members who are following either the **Flex Plan** or the **Core Plan**® on **TurnAround**.® All **Core Plan** recipes are marked with our **Core Plan** recipe icon ☑. We include *POINTS*® values so you can use any of the recipes if you are following the **Flex Plan** on the program. *POINTS* values are assigned based on calories, fat (grams), and fiber (grams) provided for a serving size of a recipe.

- All recipes feature approximate nutritional information; our recipes are analyzed for Calories (Cal), Total Fat (Fat), Saturated Fat (Sat Fat), Trans Fat (Trans Fat), Cholesterol (Chol), Sodium (Sod), Carbohydrates (Carb), Dietary Fiber (Fib), Protein (Prot), and Calcium (Calc).

- Nutritional information for recipes that include meat, poultry, and fish are based on cooked skinless boneless portions (unless otherwise stated), with the fat trimmed.

- We recommend that you buy lean meat and poultry, then trim it of all visible fat before cooking. When poultry is cooked with the skin on, we suggest removing the skin before eating.

- We follow the USDA guidelines for cooking meats and poultry to safe temperatures to prevent foodborne illness, but for beef and lamb (steaks, roasts, and chops) be aware that cooking them to the recommended minimum of 145°F will give you a medium-cooked steak, roast, or chop.

- Before serving, divide foods—including vegetables, sauce, or accompaniments—into portions of equal size according to the designated number of servings per recipe.

- Any substitutions made to the ingredients will alter the "Per serving" nutritional information and may affect the **Core Plan** recipe status or the *POINTS* value.

- It is implied that all fresh fruits, vegetables, and greens in recipes should be rinsed before using.

- All recipes use no more than 7 ingredients, take 3 steps (or less), and are ready to serve in 30 minutes (or less).

- For each chapter, the special shortcut ingredients are **highlighted in blue.**

WASABI SALMON CAKES, PAGE 53

CONTENTS

SO FRESH!

Fast food is so easy—just grab your goodies
from the produce aisle

ORANGE BEEF WITH BROCCOLI

PREP 10 MIN   COOK 10 MIN   SERVES 4

1	large navel orange
¾	pound thin-sliced top-round steak, trimmed and cut into strips
½	teaspoon salt
3	teaspoons Asian (dark) sesame oil
1	(12-ounce) bag broccoli slaw
⅛	teaspoon black pepper

1 Grate 2 teaspoons of the zest from the orange; squeeze ¾ cup of juice. Combine the steak with 1 teaspoon of the orange zest and ¼ teaspoon of the salt in a medium bowl; toss to coat. Set aside the remaining 1 teaspoon orange zest and the orange juice.

2 Heat a large nonstick skillet over medium-high heat until a drop of water sizzles on it. Add 2 teaspoons of the sesame oil and swirl to coat the pan. Add the steak mixture and stir-fry until no longer pink, about 2 minutes. Transfer to a plate.

3 Heat the remaining 1 teaspoon sesame oil in the skillet. Add the broccoli slaw and stir-fry until it begins to wilt, 3–3½ minutes. Stir in the reserved ¾ cup orange juice and cook 30 seconds. Add the steak mixture and cook, stirring frequently, until hot. Stir in the reserved 1 teaspoon orange zest, the remaining ¼ teaspoon salt, and the pepper.

PER SERVING (1 cup): 187 Cal, 6 g Fat, 2 g Sat Fat, 0 g Trans Fat, 48 mg Chol, 353 mg Sod, 11 g Carb, 3 g Fib, 22 g Prot, 46 mg Calc. *POINTS* value: *4.*

BISTRO STEAK SALAD

PREP 10 MIN   COOK 5 MIN   SERVES 4

2   (6-ounce) thin-sliced
     top-round steaks, trimmed

½   teaspoon salt

¼   teaspoon black pepper

1   (16-ounce) bag classic
     iceberg salad mix

1   pint cherry tomatoes,
     quartered

1   small red onion, thinly sliced

½   cup fat-free blue-cheese
     dressing

1 Spray a broiler rack with canola oil nonstick spray and preheat the broiler.

2 Combine the steaks, salt, and pepper in a medium bowl; toss to coat. Place the steaks on the broiler rack and broil 5 inches from the heat until cooked through, about 2 minutes on each side. Transfer to a cutting board and let cool slightly, about 2 minutes. Cut into strips.

3 Combine the salad mix, tomatoes, and red onion in a large bowl. Add the steak and the dressing; mix well. Serve at once.

PER SERVING (2¾ cups salad with 2 tablespoons dressing): 185 Cal, 3 g Fat, 1 g Sat Fat, 0 g Trans Fat, 49 mg Chol, 600 mg Sod, 17 g Carb, 4 g Fib, 22 g Prot, 60 mg Calc. **POINTS** value: **3.**

GOOD IDEA

This salad is equally tasty prepared with ¾ pound chicken cutlets instead of the steak. Prepare the recipe as directed, but broil the chicken until cooked through, 3–4 minutes on each side. By substituting chicken, you'll reduce the per-serving **POINTS** value by **1.**

ISLAND PORK AND PINEAPPLE KEBABS

PREP 10 MIN   COOK 10 MIN   SERVES 4

½ **cup reduced-sugar apricot preserves**

I **tablespoon lime juice**

I **pound pork tenderloin, trimmed and cut into 20 chunks**

16 **fresh pineapple chunks**

1¼ **teaspoons Jamaican jerk seasoning**

½ **teaspoon salt**

1 Spray a broiler rack with nonstick spray and preheat the broiler.

2 To make the glaze, combine the preserves and lime juice in a small bowl; mix well and set aside.

3 Combine the pork, pineapple, jerk seasoning, and salt in a medium bowl; toss to coat. Thread the pork and pineapple alternately on 4 (12-inch) metal skewers. Place the kebabs on the broiler rack and broil 5 inches from the heat, turning every 2 minutes, until the pork is cooked through, about 8 minutes. Brush the kebabs with half the glaze and broil I minute. Turn the kebabs, brush with the remaining glaze, and broil until lightly browned, about I minute longer.

PER SERVING (I kebab): 245 Cal, 5 g Fat, 2 g Sat Fat, 0 g Trans Fat, 72 mg Chol, 351 mg Sod, 25 g Carb, I g Fib, 26 g Prot, 20 mg Calc. *POINTS* value: *5*.

GOOD IDEA

Serve these Caribbean-style kebabs with a side of whole-wheat couscous (⅔ cup cooked couscous with each serving will increase the **POINTS** value by **2**).

PORK CHOPS WITH APPLE-ONION SAUTÉ

PREP 5 MIN   COOK 20 MIN   SERVES 4

- **2 teaspoons olive oil**
- **1 (5-ounce) container refrigerated chopped onions**
- **1 (12-ounce) bag refrigerated fresh apple slices**
- **1 cup unsweetened apple juice**
- **¾ teaspoon salt**
- **¼ teaspoon black pepper**
- **4 (¼-pound) boneless center-cut pork loin chops, trimmed**

1 To make the apple-onion sauté, heat the oil in a large nonstick skillet over medium-high heat. Add the onions and cook, stirring frequently, until crisp-tender, 2–3 minutes. Add the apples and cook, stirring occasionally, until they begin to brown, 4–5 minutes. Add the apple juice and bring to a boil. Cook until the mixture is slightly thickened, 3–4 minutes. Remove the skillet from the heat; stir in ¼ teaspoon of the salt and ⅛ teaspoon of the pepper.

2 Sprinkle the pork with the remaining ½ teaspoon salt and ⅛ teaspoon pepper.

3 Spray a ridged grill pan with nonstick spray and set over medium-high heat. Add the pork and cook until an instant-read thermometer inserted into the side of each chop registers 160°F, about 4 minutes on each side. Serve at once with the apple-onion sauté.

PER SERVING (1 pork chop with ½ cup apple-onion sauté): 288 Cal, 11 g Fat, 3 g Sat Fat, 0 g Trans Fat, 70 mg Chol, 488 mg Sod, 23 g Carb, 3 g Fib, 25 g Prot, 23 mg Calc. *POINTS* value: **6.**

PENNE WITH PEAS AND BACON

PREP **5 MIN**   COOK **20 MIN**   SERVES **4**

½ **pound penne**

1 **cup shelled fresh peas**

6 **(1-ounce) slices Canadian bacon, chopped**

1 **(5-ounce) container refrigerated chopped onions**

1 **(8-ounce) bag fresh trimmed sugar-snap peas**

½ **teaspoon salt**

⅛ **teaspoon crushed red pepper**

1 Cook the penne according to package directions, omitting the salt if desired and adding the fresh peas to the pot during the last 3 minutes of cooking. Drain, reserving 1 cup of the cooking liquid.

2 While the penne is cooking, spray a large nonstick skillet with nonstick spray and set over medium-high heat. Add the bacon and onions; cook, stirring occasionally, until the onions are lightly browned, 4–5 minutes. Add the sugar-snap peas and cook, stirring frequently, until the peas are bright green, about 3 minutes.

3 Add the pasta, peas, and ½ cup of the cooking liquid; cook, stirring frequently, until hot, about 1 minute. (If the mixture is dry, add the remaining ½ cup cooking liquid, ¼ cup at a time.) Remove the skillet from the heat, stir in the salt and crushed red pepper, and serve at once.

PER SERVING (about 1¼ cups): 379 Cal, 5 g Fat, 1 g Sat Fat, 0 g Trans Fat, 20 mg Chol, 841 mg Sod, 62 g Carb, 7 g Fib, 21 g Prot, 56 mg Calc. *POINTS* value: **7**.

**PENNE WITH PEAS
AND BACON**

ASIAN CHICKEN AND MANDARIN ORANGE SALAD

PREP 10 MIN   COOK 5 MIN   SERVES 4

- 1 (¾-pound) cooked rotisserie chicken breast, skin and bones removed and meat sliced
- 50 sprays (scant 1½ teaspoons) "Spritzer-style" Asian sesame-ginger vinaigrette dressing
- 1 (5-ounce) bag spring salad mix
- 1 (15-ounce) jar refrigerated fresh peeled and sectioned mandarin oranges, drained
- 1 large cucumber, peeled and sliced

1 Spray the chicken 10 times with th **& More** Heat a medium nonstick skillet over medium-high heat. Add the chicken and cook, stirring occasionally, until heated through, about 2 minutes.

2 Transfer the chicken to a large bowl and add the salad mix, oranges, and cucumber. Spray the salad 40 more times with the dressing, tossing with tongs until lightly coated. Serve at once.

PER SERVING (3 cups): 192 Cal, 4 g Fat, 1 g Sat Fat, 0 g Trans Fat, 72 mg Chol, 242 mg Sod, 10 g Carb, 2 g Fib, 28 g Prot, 49 mg Calc. *POINTS* value: **4.**

EXPRESS LANE

Use a 10-ounce package sliced grilled chicken breast instead of boning and skinning the rotisserie chicken.

SPINACH SALAD WITH GRILLED CHICKEN

PREP 10 MIN   COOK 10 MIN   SERVES 4

4	(¼-pound) skinless, boneless chicken-breast halves
½	teaspoon salt
¼	teaspoon black pepper
½	cup fat-free raspberry vinaigrette dressing
1	(5-ounce) bag baby spinach
4	navel oranges, peeled and cut into sections
¼	cup thinly sliced red onion

1 Sprinkle the chicken with ¼ teaspoon of the salt and ⅛ teaspoon of the pepper. Spray a ridged grill pan with canola oil nonstick spray and set over medium-high heat. Add the chicken and cook until cooked through, 5–6 minutes on each side.

2 Meanwhile, place 1 tablespoon of the dressing in a cup and set aside. Combine the spinach, orange, red onion, the remaining dressing, and the remaining ¼ teaspoon salt and ⅛ teaspoon pepper in a large bowl; toss to coat. Divide among 4 bowls.

3 Transfer the chicken to a cutting board and thinly slice. Top each salad with one fourth of the chicken. Drizzle with the reserved dressing and serve at once.

PER SERVING (about 2 cups): 264 Cal, 4 g Fat, 1 g Sat Fat, 0 g Trans Fat, 68 mg Chol, 684 mg Sod, 30 g Carb, 5 g Fib, 28 g Prot, 128 mg Calc. *POINTS* value: **5.**

FOOD NOTE

Instead of navel oranges, experiment with different citrus fruits in this salad—for example, blood oranges, tangerines, or clementines (you'll need about 2 cups citrus sections).

CHICKEN WITH FRUIT SALSA

CHICKEN WITH FRUIT SALSA

PREP 10 MIN   COOK 10 MIN   SERVES 4

4 (¼-pound) skinless, boneless chicken-breast halves

½ teaspoon salt

½ teaspoon ground cumin

4 cups store-bought fresh fruit salad (such as oranges, strawberries, blueberries, seedless grapes, and watermelon)

¼ cup chopped red onion

2 tablespoons chopped fresh cilantro

1 tablespoon lime juice

1 Sprinkle both sides of the chicken with ¼ teaspoon of the salt and the cumin. Spray a ridged grill pan with canola oil nonstick spray and set over medium-high heat. Add the chicken; cook until cooked through, 5–6 minutes on each side.

2 Meanwhile, to make the salsa, combine the fruit salad, red onion, cilantro, lime juice, and the remaining ¼ teaspoon salt in a bowl.

3 Serve the chicken with the salsa on the side.

PER SERVING (1 chicken-breast half with 1 cup salsa): 230 Cal, 4 g Fat, 1 g Sat Fat, 0 g Trans Fat, 68 mg Chol, 359 mg Sod, 24 g Carb, 3 g Fib, 26 g Prot, 43 mg Calc. **POINTS** value: **4.**

PLAN AHEAD

Double the recipe and serve the leftovers chilled. Let the grilled chicken cool completely; then wrap in plastic wrap. Transfer the fruit salsa to an airtight container. Refrigerate the chicken and the salsa up to 2 days.

SPEEDY MOO SHU CHICKEN

PREP 10 MIN   COOK 10 MIN   SERVES 4

¾   **pound skinless, boneless chicken thighs, cut into strips**

1   **(4-ounce) package sliced fresh shiitake mushrooms**

⅛   **teaspoon salt**

3   **cups coleslaw mix**

2   **tablespoons hoisin sauce**

4   **(7-inch) fat-free flour tortillas**

1 To make the filling, spray a medium nonstick skillet with nonstick spray and set over medium-high heat. Add the chicken and cook, stirring occasionally, until lightly browned and cooked through, 5–6 minutes; transfer to a large plate.

2 Spray the skillet with more nonstick spray. Add the mushrooms and salt; cook, stirring occasionally, until the mushrooms are softened, 2–3 minutes. Add the coleslaw mix and cook, stirring occasionally, until the coleslaw is wilted, 2–3 minutes. Add the chicken and cook, stirring frequently, until heated through, about 1 minute. Remove the skillet from the heat and stir in the hoisin sauce. Serve at once.

PER SERVING (1 roll): 269 Cal, 7 g Fat, 2 g Sat Fat, 0 g Trans Fat, 53 mg Chol, 621 mg Sod, 29 g Carb, 5 g Fib, 23 g Prot, 122 mg Calc. *POINTS* value: *5.*

GOOD IDEA

Round out this meal with some steamed broccoli drizzled with a touch of Asian (dark) sesame oil (1½ cups cooked broccoli with 1 teaspoon sesame oil for each person will increase the **POINTS** value by **1**).

SAUSAGE-MUSHROOM RISOTTO

PREP **5 MIN**   COOK **25 MIN**   SERVES **4**

- 1 **(32-ounce) carton reduced-sodium chicken broth**
- ½ **pound Italian turkey sausage links, casings removed**
- 1 **(4-ounce) package sliced fresh exotic mushrooms**
- 2 **teaspoons chopped fresh thyme**
- 1 **cup Arborio rice**
- 2 **tablespoons grated Parmesan cheese**

1 Bring the broth to a boil in a saucepan. Reduce the heat and keep at a simmer.

2 Meanwhile, spray a large saucepan with nonstick spray and set over high heat. Add the sausage and cook until no longer pink, 3–4 minutes, stirring with a wooden spoon to break it up. Add the mushrooms and thyme; cook, stirring frequently, until the mushrooms begin to soften, about 2 minutes. Stir in the rice, reduce the heat, and cook, stirring constantly, until the rice is well coated, about 1 minute. Add 1 cup of the broth and cook, stirring constantly, until the liquid is absorbed, 1–2 minutes.

3 Continue adding the broth, ½ cup at a time, stirring until it is absorbed before adding more. Cook just until the rice is tender, 18–20 minutes. Remove the saucepan from the heat and stir in the cheese. Serve at once.

PER SERVING (1 cup): 332 Cal, 7 g Fat, 2 g Sat Fat, 0 g Trans Fat, 55 mg Chol, 960 mg Sod, 42 g Carb, 1 g Fib, 23 g Prot, 87 mg Calc. *POINTS* value: **7.**

QUICK CALDO VERDE

PREP **5 MIN**   COOK **25 MIN**   SERVES **4**

½ **pound turkey kielbasa, sliced**

1   **(5-ounce) container refrigerated chopped onions**

1   **teaspoon smoked paprika**

2   **(14½-ounce) cans reduced-sodium chicken broth**

1   **(18-ounce) bag refrigerated fully-cooked sliced potatoes**

4   **cups fresh cut-up kale**

1 Spray a large saucepan with nonstick spray and set over medium-high heat. Add the kielbasa and cook, stirring, until lightly browned, 4–5 minutes; transfer to a plate.

2 Add the onions and paprika to the skillet; cook, stirring, until the onions are crisp-tender, about 1 minute. Add the broth, 1 cup water, and potatoes; bring to a boil. Cook until the potatoes are very soft, 4–5 minutes.

3 Coarsely mash the potatoes with a wooden spoon. Stir in the kale and return to a boil. Reduce the heat and simmer, covered, until the kale is tender, about 10 minutes. Stir in the kielbasa and cook until the flavors are blended, about 5 minutes longer.

PER SERVING (1½ cups): 214 Cal, 6 g Fat, 2 g Sat Fat, 0 g Trans Fat, 29 mg Chol, 1,233 mg Sod, 27 g Carb, 3 g Fib, 16 g Prot, 114 mg Calc. **POINTS** value: **4**.

GOOD IDEA

Serve this hearty Portuguese-style soup with a basket of warm high-fiber rolls (a 2-ounce roll will increase the per-serving **POINTS** value by **1**).

QUICK CALDO VERDE

LEMONY TUNA SALAD NIÇOISE

PREP 10 MIN   COOK 20 MIN   SERVES 4

1 (12-ounce) bag fresh trimmed green beans

4 teaspoons extra-virgin olive oil

1 tablespoon lemon juice

¼ teaspoon salt

1 (5-ounce) bag mixed spring greens

2 (6-ounce) cans solid white tuna in water, drained and flaked

20 pitted kalamata olives (about ⅓ cup)

1 Bring a large saucepan of lightly salted water to a boil. Add the green beans, return the water to a boil, and cook until the beans are crisp-tender, about 3 minutes. Rinse under cold running water; drain and transfer to a medium bowl.

2 To make the dressing, combine the oil, lemon juice, and salt in a small bowl, beating with a whisk until blended. Combine the spring greens and 1 tablespoon of the dressing; toss to coat. Transfer the greens to a platter. Place the tuna in the center of the platter.

3 Add the remaining dressing to the green beans; toss to coat. Place the green beans around the tuna, sprinkle the salad with the olives, and serve at once.

PER SERVING (about 2 cups): 185 Cal, 7 g Fat, 1 g Sat Fat, 0 g Trans Fat, 23 mg Chol, 598 mg Sod, 9 g Carb, 4 g Fib, 22 g Prot, 75 mg Calc. **POINTS** value: **3**.

GOOD IDEA

For a more substantial dish, place some peeled hard-cooked eggs (from a salad bar), cut into quarters, around the tuna in step 3 (½ hard-cooked egg with each serving will increase the **POINTS** value by **1**).

BLACKENED-SHRIMP CAESAR SALAD

PREP 5 MIN   COOK 10 MIN   SERVES 4

1½ **pounds extra-large peeled and deveined shrimp**

2 **teaspoons Cajun seasoning**

1 **(10-ounce) bag Caesar salad mix with light dressing**

1 **(5-ounce) bag romaine salad mix**

1 Sprinkle the shrimp with the Cajun seasoning. Spray a ridged grill pan with nonstick spray and set over medium-high heat. Add half the shrimp and cook just until lightly browned and opaque in the center, about 2 minutes on each side. Transfer to a plate. Spray the pan with more nonstick spray and repeat with the remaining shrimp.

2 Meanwhile, combine the lettuce and cheese from the Caesar salad mix and the romaine salad mix in a large bowl. Add the croutons and dressing from the Caesar salad mix; toss well to coat.

3 Divide the salad among 4 bowls; top evenly with the shrimp and serve at once.

PER SERVING (about 6 shrimp with about 2 cups salad): 213 Cal, 4 g Fat, 1 g Sat Fat, 0 g Trans Fat, 244 mg Chol, 1,101 mg Sod, 15 g Carb, 3 g Fib, 29 g Prot, 126 mg Calc. *POINTS* value: *4.*

FOOD NOTE

You can also prepare this salad with large shrimp, which are less expensive. Just reduce the cooking time to about 1½ minutes on each side.

SCALLOP AND VEGETABLE STIR-FRY

PREP 10 MIN   COOK 10 MIN   SERVES 4

2   teaspoons canola oil

1½ pounds sea scallops

1   teaspoon Asian (dark) sesame oil

1   (12-ounce) bag assorted fresh vegetables cut for stir-fry

1   tablespoon minced peeled fresh ginger

2   garlic cloves, minced

1½ tablespoons reduced-sodium soy sauce

1 Heat a large nonstick skillet or wok over medium-high heat until a drop of water sizzles on it. Add the canola oil and swirl to coat the pan. Add the scallops and stir-fry just until opaque in the center, about 3 minutes on each side. Transfer to a plate.

2 Heat the sesame oil in the skillet. Add the vegetables and stir-fry just until tender, about 1 minute. Add the ginger and garlic; stir-fry just until fragrant, about 1 minute. Stir in ¼ cup water and cook, covered, until the vegetables are crisp-tender, about 1 minute. Stir in the scallops and soy sauce; cook, uncovered, stirring frequently, until heated through, about 30 seconds. Serve at once.

PER SERVING (about 1 cup): 164 Cal, 5 g Fat, 1 g Sat Fat, 0 g Trans Fat, 45 mg Chol, 432 mg Sod, 8 g Carb, 2 g Fib, 22 g Prot, 126 mg Calc. *POINTS* value: *3*.

GOOD IDEA

Serve this dish with a side of instant rice (½ cup cooked rice, brown or white, per serving will increase the *POINTS* value by *2*).

CREAM OF BROCCOLI SOUP

PREP 5 MIN   COOK 25 MIN   SERVES 4

2 (14½-ounce) cans reduced-sodium chicken broth

2 (12-ounce) bags fresh broccoli florets

1 (5-ounce) container refrigerated chopped onions

1 celery stalk, chopped

1 cup fat-free half-and-half

⅛ teaspoon ground nutmeg

1 Combine the broth, broccoli, onions, and celery in a large saucepan; bring to a boil. Reduce the heat and cook, covered, until the vegetables are tender, 13–15 minutes. Let the broccoli mixture cool about 5 minutes.

2 Pour the mixture into a blender in batches and puree. Return the mixture to the pan and stir in the remaining ingredients. Cook, stirring occasionally, over medium heat just until heated through, about 1 minute longer.

PER SERVING (about 1½ cups): 125 Cal, 2 g Fat, 1 g Sat Fat, 0 g Trans Fat, 3 mg Chol, 992 mg Sod, 21 g Carb, 5 g Fib, 10 g Prot, 167 mg Calc. *POINTS* value: *2*.

GOOD IDEA

For a satisfying main-dish soup, stir in 2 cups diced cooked chicken breast with the remaining ingredients in step 2 (the per-serving *POINTS* value will increase by *2*).

MUSHROOM AND TOFU STIR-FRY

PREP 5 MIN   **COOK** 10 MIN   **SERVES** 4

3 teaspoons Asian (dark) sesame oil

1 (14-ounce) package light firm tofu, drained and cubed

2 (4-ounce) packages sliced fresh exotic mushrooms

4 scallions, chopped

¼ cup hoisin sauce

1 Heat a large nonstick skillet or wok over medium-high heat until a drop of water sizzles on it. Add 1 teaspoon of the sesame oil and swirl to coat the pan. Add the tofu and stir-fry until lightly golden, 5–6 minutes. Transfer to a bowl.

2 Heat the remaining 2 teaspoons sesame oil in the skillet. Add the mushrooms and stir-fry until lightly browned, 5–6 minutes. Add the tofu and stir-fry until hot, about 1 minute. Add the scallions and stir-fry just until wilted, about 30 seconds. Add the hoisin sauce and cook, stirring constantly, just until blended, about 10 seconds longer. Serve at once.

PER SERVING (¾ cup): 167 Cal, 9 g Fat, 1 Sat Fat, 0 g Trans Fat, 0 mg Chol, 264 mg Sod, 15 g Carb, 4 g Fib, 11 g Prot, 68 mg Calc. *POINTS* value: *3*.

GOOD IDEA

To give this recipe a little crunch, add ¼ cup unsalted dry-roasted peanuts with the scallions in step 2 (you'll increase the per-serving *POINTS* value by *1*).

PORTOBELLO CHEESEBURGERS

PREP **5 MIN**   COOK **10 MIN**   SERVES **4**

4   **(3-ounce) fresh Portobello mushroom caps**

¼   **teaspoon salt**

¼   **teaspoon black pepper**

4   **(¾-ounce) slices reduced-fat Swiss cheese**

4   **light multigrain English muffins, split**

1   **large jarred roasted red pepper, drained and sliced**

8   **teaspoons fat-free balsamic vinaigrette dressing**

1 Spray the mushrooms with nonstick spray and sprinkle with the salt and black pepper. Heat a ridged grill pan over medium-high heat. Add the mushrooms, rounded side up, and cook until they begin to release their liquid, about 4 minutes. Turn and cook rounded side down until almost tender, about 2 minutes. Top each mushroom with 1 slice of the cheese and cook until the cheese is melted and the mushrooms are tender, 1–2 minutes longer.

2 Meanwhile, toast the muffins.

3 Layer 1 mushroom, one quarter of the roasted pepper, and 2 teaspoons of the dressing on the bottom half of each muffin. Cover with the muffins tops and serve at once.

PER SERVING (1 cheeseburger): 211 Cal, 3 g Fat, 1 g Sat Fat, 0 g Trans Fat, 7 mg Chol, 668 mg Sod, 34 g Carb, 4 g Fib, 15 g Prot, 318 mg Calc. *POINTS* value: **4.**

TRY IT

The Portobello (pawr-tuh-BEH-loh), a mature variety of the cremini mushroom, is readily available at supermarkets. Because the moisture content of the Portobello is lower than that of other fresh mushrooms, it takes on a delicious meaty texture when cooked. So consider Portobellos a tasty alternative the next time you crave a burger or a steak.

SAUSAGE-STUFFED MUSHROOMS

PREP 10 MIN   COOK 20 MIN   SERVES 4

½   **pound sweet Italian turkey-sausage links, casings removed**

½   **cup finely chopped fennel**

¼   **cup plain or seasoned dried bread crumbs**

4   **(4-inch) fresh Portobello mushroom caps**

2   **tablespoons grated Parmesan cheese**

1   Preheat the oven to 425°F. Spray a baking sheet with nonstick spray.

2   Combine the sausage, fennel, and bread crumbs in a bowl. Spoon the sausage mixture into each mushroom cap, mounding it slightly in the center. Sprinkle with the cheese; spray lightly with nonstick spray.

3   Cover the mushrooms loosely with foil and bake 15 minutes. Uncover and bake until the mushrooms are browned and cooked through, about 5 minutes longer.

PER SERVING (1 stuffed mushroom): 189 Cal, 8 g Fat, 2 g Sat Fat, 0 g Trans Fat, 55 mg Chol, 509 mg Sod, 11 g Carb, 2 g Fib, 19 g Prot, 90 mg Calc. *POINTS* value: **4**.

FOOD NOTE

If fresh fennel is not available at your grocery store, substitute an equal amount of chopped celery.

ROASTED BUTTERNUT SQUASH

PREP 5 MIN   **COOK** 25 MIN   **SERVES** 4 (AS A SIDE DISH)

1	**(20-ounce) package peeled cut-up butternut squash**
2	**tablespoons maple syrup**
1	**tablespoon olive oil**
1	**teaspoon curry powder**
¾	**teaspoon salt**
⅛	**teaspoon cayenne**

1 Preheat the oven to 450°F. Spray a large baking sheet with nonstick spray.

2 Combine all the ingredients in a large bowl; toss well to coat. Place the squash mixture in one layer on the baking sheet.

3 Bake, stirring every 10 minutes, until the squash is tender, 23–25 minutes.

PER SERVING (about ½ cup): 107 Cal, 4 g Fat, 1 g Sat Fat, 0 g Trans Fat, 0 mg Chol, 448 mg Sod, 20 g Carb, 2 g Fib, 1 g Prot, 60 mg Calc. **POINTS** value: **2**.

GOOD IDEA

Serve this rustic side dish with our Duck with Port and Fig Glaze (p. 96) or a simple pan-seared pork chop (a cooked 3-ounce bone-in chop will increase the per-serving **POINTS** value by **3**).

CABBAGE, FENNEL, AND CARROT SLAW

PREP **5 MIN**   COOK **NONE**   SERVES **6 (AS A SIDE DISH)**

6   **tablespoons reduced-fat mayonnaise**

2   **tablespoons apple-cider vinegar**

½   **teaspoon salt**

1   **(8- or 10-ounce) bag shredded red cabbage**

1   **fennel bulb, trimmed and thinly sliced**

1   **cup shredded carrots**

1 Combine the mayonnaise, vinegar, and salt in a large bowl, beating with a whisk until blended.

2 Add the cabbage, fennel, and carrots; toss well to coat.

PER SERVING (about ¾ cup): 81 Cal, 5 g Fat, 1 g Sat Fat, 0 g Trans Fat, 5 mg Chol, 357 mg Sod, 9 g Carb, 3 g Fib, 1 g Prot, 48 mg Calc. *POINTS* value: *1.*

GOOD IDEA

Serve this colorful slaw with grilled chicken (a ¼-pound chicken-breast half, cooked, will increase the **POINTS** value by **4**).

GRAPEFRUIT, JICAMA, AND OLIVE SALAD

PREP 10 MIN   COOK NONE   SERVES 4 (AS A SIDE DISH)

1   tablespoon lemon juice

2   teaspoons extra-virgin olive oil

¼   teaspoon salt

⅛   teaspoon black pepper

1   (24-ounce) jar refrigerated fresh red grapefruit sections in lightly sweetened fruit juice, drained

½   jicama, peeled and cut into thin strips

10 pitted kalamata olives, sliced

1 Combine the lemon juice, oil, salt, and pepper in a large bowl, beating with a whisk until blended.

2 Add the grapefruit, jicama, and olives; toss well to coat and serve at once.

PER SERVING (1¼ cups): 123 Cal, 4 g Fat, 1 g Sat Fat, 0 g Trans Fat, 0 mg Chol, 253 mg Sod, 23 g Carb, 6 g Fib, 2 g Prot, 48 mg Calc. *POINTS* value: **2.**

GOOD IDEA

For a tropical seafood salad, stir in 1 pound cooked shrimp (the per-serving **POINTS** value will increase by **2**).

2

A CAN AND A PLAN

Pop open a can and presto! You've got
good-for-you meals in no time flat

GLAZED STEAK WITH ROASTED VEGETABLES

PREP 10 MIN   **COOK** 20 MIN   **SERVES** 4

---

1 (14½-ounce) can whole new potatoes, rinsed, drained, and halved

1 (14-ounce) can whole peeled plum tomatoes, drained

½ pound assorted color bell peppers, sliced

¾ cup balsamic vinegar

1 (1-pound) flank steak, trimmed

½ teaspoon black pepper

¼ cup fresh basil leaves, torn

1 Preheat the oven to 500°F. Place the potatoes, tomatoes, and bell peppers in a small roasting pan; spray with olive oil nonstick spray. Roast until the potatoes are lightly browned, about 20 minutes.

2 Meanwhile, to make the glaze, bring the vinegar to a boil in a small saucepan. Reduce the heat and simmer until the vinegar is syrupy and reduced to about ¼ cup, about 6 minutes. Set aside and keep warm.

3 Lightly spray the steak with olive oil nonstick spray; sprinkle with the black pepper. Heat a ridged grill pan over medium heat. Add the steak and cook until an instant-read thermometer inserted into the side registers 145°F for medium, about 8 minutes on each side. Transfer to a cutting board and cut into 12 slices. Drizzle the glaze over the steak and sprinkle the basil over the vegetables.

PER SERVING (3 slices steak with about ½ cup vegetables and 1 tablespoon glaze): 275 Cal, 10 g Fat, 3 g Sat Fat, 0 g Trans Fat, 46 mg Chol, 300 mg Sod, 17 g Carb, 4 g Fib, 27 g Prot, 46 mg Calc. *POINTS* value: **6.**

GLAZED STEAK WITH
ROASTED VEGETABLES

CHIPOTLE BEEF WITH HOMINY-POTATO MASH

PREP **5 MIN**   COOK **25 MIN**   SERVES **4**

- **1 pound Yukon Gold potatoes, peeled and diced**
- **1 (15-ounce) can white hominy, rinsed and drained**
- **1 chipotle en adobo, seeded and minced + 1 tablespoon of the adobo sauce**
- **½ teaspoon salt**
- **1 (1-pound) flank steak, trimmed**
- **1 large white onion, thinly sliced**
- **1 large orange bell pepper, thinly sliced**

1 Bring to a boil in a large saucepan the potatoes, hominy, and enough water to cover by 2 inches. Cook until the potatoes are fork-tender, about 18 minutes. Drain, reserving 1 cup of the cooking liquid. Return the potatoes and hominy to the saucepan. Add the cooking liquid, chipotle en adobo, and ¼ teaspoon of the salt. Coarsely mash.

2 Meanwhile, slice the beef into strips. Spray a large nonstick skillet with nonstick spray and set over medium-high heat. Add the beef and cook, stirring constantly, just until cooked through, about 2 minutes. Transfer to a bowl; add the adobo sauce and toss to coat.

3 Spray the skillet again with nonstick spray and set over medium-high heat. Add the onion and bell pepper; cook, stirring occasionally, until the vegetables are crisp-tender, about 5 minutes. Add the beef mixture and the remaining ¼ teaspoon salt; cook, stirring occasionally, until heated through, about 2 minutes. Serve with the hominy-potato mash.

PER SERVING (1 cup beef mixture with ¾ cup hominy-potato mash): 349 Cal, 8 g Fat, 3 g Sat Fat, 0 g Trans Fat, 46 mg Chol, 652 mg Sod, 40 g Carb, 6 g Fib, 28 g Prot, 39 mg Calc. **POINTS** value: **7.**

PORK WITH BAKED BEAN SUCCOTASH

PREP 5 MIN   COOK 10 MIN   SERVES 6

1 (16-ounce) can baked beans with maple-cured bacon, drained, with ¼ cup of the sauce reserved

1 (11-ounce) can yellow and white corn kernels, drained

3 scallions, thinly sliced

1 tablespoon apple-cider vinegar

1 teaspoon ground coriander

6 (¼-pound) boneless pork loin chops, trimmed

1 To make the succotash, combine the baked beans, corn, and scallions in a small saucepan. Cook, covered, over low heat, stirring occasionally, until heated through, about 8 minutes. Set aside and keep warm.

2 Meanwhile, combine the vinegar, coriander, and the reserved bean sauce in a small bowl.

3 Spray a large nonstick skillet with nonstick spray and set over medium-high heat. Add the pork chops and cook until golden brown on one side, 4–5 minutes. Turn and cook, brushing with the vinegar sauce mixture, until an instant-read thermometer inserted into the side of each chop registers 160°F, 4–5 minutes longer. Serve with the succotash.

PER SERVING (1 pork chop with about ⅓ cup succotash): 316 Cal, 11 g Fat, 4 g Sat Fat, 0 g Trans Fat, 61 mg Chol, 333 mg Sod, 31 g Carb, 4 g Fib, 25 g Prot, 61 mg Calc. **POINTS** value: **6.**

ZAP IT

To prepare the succotash even more quickly, combine the baked beans, corn, and scallions in a 1-quart microwavable bowl. Cover with plastic wrap; then prick a few holes in the plastic. Microwave on High until heated through, 3 minutes.

LEMON CHICKEN WITH
CARROT-BASIL SAUCE

LEMON CHICKEN WITH CARROT-BASIL SAUCE

PREP 15 MIN   COOK 10 MIN   SERVES 6

- 1 (15½-ounce) can cannellini beans, rinsed and drained
- 1 (12-ounce) can carrot juice
- ⅔ cup fresh basil leaves
- ½ teaspoon salt
- ½ teaspoon black pepper
- 1 large lemon
- 6 (¼-pound) chicken cutlets

1 To make the sauce, puree the beans, carrot juice, and ⅓ cup of the basil in a blender. Transfer to a small saucepan; stir in ¼ teaspoon of the salt and ¼ teaspoon of the pepper. Cook over low heat, stirring occasionally, just until hot, about 5 minutes. Remove the saucepan from the heat; cover and keep warm.

2 Meanwhile, thinly slice the remaining ⅓ cup basil and set aside. Grate 2 teaspoons of the zest from the lemon; squeeze ¼ cup of juice. Combine the lemon zest, lemon juice, and the remaining ¼ teaspoon salt and ¼ teaspoon pepper; brush over the chicken.

3 Spray a ridged grill pan with nonstick spray and set over medium-high heat. Add the chicken and cook just until cooked through, 3–4 minutes on each side. Sprinkle with the reserved basil and serve with the sauce.

PER SERVING (1 chicken cutlet with ⅓ cup sauce): 236 Cal, 4 g Fat, 1 g Sat Fat, 0 g Trans Fat, 68 mg Chol, 431 mg Sod, 19 g Carb, 4 g Fib, 30 g Prot, 81 mg Calc. *POINTS* value: 4.

CARIBBEAN PORK WITH GRILLED-PINEAPPLE SALSA

PREP 15 MIN   COOK 10 MIN   SERVES 6

1 **(20-ounce) can pineapple rings in juice, drained**

1 **large lime**

2 **(¾-pound) pork tenderloins, each trimmed, cut crosswise into 6 pieces, and pounded to a 1-inch thickness**

2 **teaspoons Jamaican jerk seasoning**

1 **small red onion, cut crosswise into 4 (¼-inch-thick) slices**

3 **celery stalks, thinly sliced**

⅓ **cup chopped fresh cilantro**

1 Spray a grill rack with olive oil nonstick spray; preheat the grill to medium-high. Drain the pineapple on paper towels. Grate ½ teaspoon of the zest from the lime; squeeze 3 tablespoons of juice. Brush the pork with 2 tablespoons of the lime juice; then sprinkle it with the jerk seasoning.

2 Spray the pineapple, pork, and red onion with olive oil nonstick spray; place on the grill rack. Grill the pineapple and red onion until lightly charred, about 3 minutes on each side. Grill the pork until an instant-read thermometer inserted into the side of each piece registers 160°F, about 5 minutes on each side.

3 Dice the pineapple and red onion. Combine the pineapple, red onion, celery, cilantro, the reserved lime zest, and the remaining 1 tablespoon lime juice in a bowl. Serve with the pork.

PER SERVING (2 pieces pork with ⅓ cup salsa): 209 Cal, 6 g Fat, 2 g Sat Fat, 0 g Trans Fat, 67 mg Chol, 70 mg Sod, 14 g Carb, 2 g Fib, 25 g Prot, 36 mg Calc. *POINTS* value: 4.

CURRIED CHICKEN-LENTIL BURGERS

PREP 10 MIN   COOK 15 MIN   SERVES 4

⅓   cup plain fat-free yogurt

2   teaspoons Madras curry powder

¾   pound ground skinless chicken breast

1   (15-ounce) can lentils, rinsed and drained

2   scallions, chopped

2   tablespoons cornmeal

8   large Boston lettuce leaves

1 Combine the yogurt and curry powder in a medium bowl, beating with a whisk until blended. Add the chicken, lentils, scallions, and cornmeal; mix just until combined. Form the mixture into 4 (1-inch-thick) patties.

2 Spray a large nonstick skillet with canola oil nonstick spray and set over medium heat. Add the patties and cook until an instant-read thermometer inserted into the side of each one registers 165°F, about 6 minutes on each side.

3 Wrap each burger in 2 lettuce leaves and serve at once.

PER SERVING (1 burger): 225 Cal, 3 g Fat, 1 g Sat Fat, 0 g Trans Fat, 52 mg Chol, 237 mg Sod, 21 g Carb, 5 g Fib, 27 g Prot, 84 mg Calc. *POINTS* value: *4.*

HOW WE DID IT

For the easiest prep, we dampened our hands with cold water before shaping the chicken mixture into patties so it wouldn't stick.

PENNE WITH CHICKEN-ARTICHOKE MARINARA

PREP 10 MIN   COOK 20 MIN   SERVES 6

- 1 **(12-ounce) package multigrain penne**
- 1 **(25¾-ounce) can light spaghetti sauce**
- 1 **pound yellow squash, halved lengthwise and cut into ½-inch slices**
- 1 **(14-ounce) can water-packed quartered artichoke hearts, drained**
- 3 **garlic cloves, minced**
- 2 **cups shredded cooked chicken breast**
- ½ **teaspoon crushed red pepper**

1 Cook the penne according to package directions, omitting the salt if desired.

2 Meanwhile, to make the sauce, combine the spaghetti sauce, squash, artichokes, and garlic in a large saucepan; bring to a simmer over medium heat. Reduce the heat and cook, covered, just until the squash is tender, about 10 minutes. Remove the saucepan from the heat; stir in the chicken.

3 Combine the penne and sauce in a large bowl; toss to coat. Sprinkle with the crushed red pepper and serve at once.

PER SERVING (1 cup penne with 1 cup sauce): 377 Cal, 3 g Fat, 1 g Sat Fat, 0 g Trans Fat, 38 mg Chol, 776 mg Sod, 63 g Carb, 8 g Fib, 26 g Prot, 72 mg Calc. *POINTS* value: **7**.

GOOD IDEA

Serve this hearty dish with a peppery arugula salad (1½ cups baby arugula leaves tossed with 1 tablespoon creamy reduced-calorie salad dressing for each serving will increase the *POINTS* value by *1*).

GRILLED TURKEY TONNATO

PREP 10 MIN   COOK 10 MIN   SERVES 6

1 lemon

1 (6-ounce) can solid light tuna in olive oil (do not drain)

1 large hard-cooked egg, peeled

2 teaspoons Dijon mustard

3 teaspoons capers, rinsed and drained

3 tablespoons chopped fresh flat-leaf parsley

6 (¼-pound) turkey cutlets

1 To make the sauce, grate the zest from the lemon and set aside; squeeze 2 tablespoons of juice. Puree the tuna, ¼ cup water, lemon juice, egg, mustard, and 2 teaspoons of the capers in a blender until almost smooth. Transfer to a bowl and stir in the parsley.

2 Spray the cutlets with nonstick spray. Heat a ridged grill pan over medium heat. Add the cutlets and cook until browned and cooked through, about 4 minutes on each side.

3 Spread ½ cup of the sauce on a serving platter. Top with the cutlets, the remaining sauce, the reserved lemon zest, and the remaining 1 teaspoon capers.

PER SERVING (1 turkey cutlet with ¼ cup sauce): 221 Cal, 8 g Fat, 2 g Sat Fat, 0 g Trans Fat, 115 mg Chol, 230 mg Sod, 1 g Carb, 0 g Fib, 35 g Prot, 26 mg Calc. *POINTS* value: **5.**

PLAN AHEAD

This dish is also delicious served chilled. Cover the platter with plastic wrap and refrigerate up to 4 hours.

TURKEY-BEAN CHILI

PREP 10 MIN   COOK 20 MIN   SERVES 4

I   **pound skinless, boneless turkey breast, cut into 1-inch cubes**

I   **onion, chopped**

I   **tablespoon chili powder**

I   **(15½-ounce) can pinto beans, rinsed and drained**

I   **(14½-ounce) can diced tomatoes with jalapeño peppers**

I   **(11-ounce) can Mexican-style corn kernels**

⅓   **cup chopped fresh cilantro**

1 Spray a nonstick Dutch oven with olive oil nonstick spray and set over medium-high heat. Add the turkey and onion; cook, stirring frequently, until the turkey is no longer pink, about 5 minutes. Stir in the chili powder.

2 Add the beans, tomatoes, and corn; bring to a boil. Reduce the heat and simmer, covered, until the turkey is cooked through and the flavors are blended, about 15 minutes. Stir in the cilantro and serve at once.

PER SERVING (1½ cups): 324 Cal, 3 g Fat, 1 g Sat Fat, 0 g Trans Fat, 75 mg Chol, 530 mg Sod, 41 g Carb, 10 g Fib, 36 g Prot, 94 mg Calc. **POINTS** value: **6**.

GOOD IDEA

Garnish each serving with 1 tablespoon fat-free sour cream and extra chopped fresh cilantro (the **POINTS** value will remain the same). You can also increase the chili powder to 2 tablespoons if you prefer your chili on the spicier side.

PASTA WITH SAUSAGE, PEAS, AND MUSTARD GREENS

PREP 10 MIN   COOK 20 MIN   SERVES 6

½   **pound orecchiette**

4   **Italian turkey sausage links (¾ pound), halved lengthwise and cut into ¾-inch pieces**

3   **garlic cloves, minced**

1   **(15½-ounce) can black-eyed peas, rinsed and drained**

1   **(14½-ounce) can vegetable broth**

1   **(14-ounce) can seasoned mustard greens**

2   **tablespoons grated Parmesan cheese**

1 Cook the orecchiette according to package directions, omitting the salt if desired.

2 Meanwhile, to make the sauce, spray a nonstick Dutch oven with nonstick spray and set over medium-high heat. Add the sausage and cook, stirring occasionally, until no longer pink, about 5 minutes. Add the garlic and cook, stirring frequently, until fragrant, about 1 minute. Add the black-eyed peas, broth, and mustard greens; bring to a simmer. Reduce the heat and cook, covered, until the sausage is cooked through, about 5 minutes.

3 Add the pasta to the sauce; toss to coat. Cook, stirring occasionally, until well mixed, about 1 minute. Sprinkle with the cheese and serve at once.

PER SERVING (1⅓ cups): 361 Cal, 8 g Fat, 2 g Sat Fat, 0 g Trans Fat, 54 mg Chol, 990 mg Sod, 46 g Carb, 6 g Fib, 26 g Prot, 131 mg Calc. *POINTS* value: **7**.

TRY IT

This chunky sauce is gutsy enough to stand up to whole-wheat pasta, so substitute whole-wheat fusilli or penne for the orecchiette if you like. You'll also reduce the per-serving *POINTS* value by **1**.

THAI TUNA SALAD

PREP 15 MIN   COOK NONE   SERVES 4

1   lime, halved

2   (6-ounce) cans solid white tuna in water, drained and flaked

1   (¾-pound) ripe papaya, peeled, seeded, and cut into 2-inch-thick strips

¼   cup canned pickled red jalapeño wheels, drained and chopped

¼   cup dry-roasted peanuts, coarsely chopped

¼   cup fresh basil leaves, chopped

2   scallions, thinly sliced

1 Squeeze the juice from half the lime; cut the remaining half into 4 wedges.

2 Combine the tuna, papaya, jalapeño wheels, peanuts, basil, scallions, and lime juice in a medium bowl; toss gently to combine. Serve at once with the lime wedges.

PER SERVING (¾ cup with 1 lime wedge): 174 Cal, 5 g Fat, 1 g Sat Fat, 0 g Trans Fat, 23 mg Chol, 447 mg Sod, 10 g Carb, 2 g Fib, 23 g Prot, 41 mg Calc. *POINTS* value: *3.*

MAKE IT CORE

It's easy to enjoy this salad on the **Core Plan**. Instead of the pickled jalapeño wheels, use 2 fresh jalapeño peppers, seeded and chopped (wear gloves to prevent irritation), and omit the nuts (the per-serving **POINTS** value will decrease by *1*).

WASABI SALMON CAKES

WASABI SALMON CAKES

PREP 10 MIN   COOK 10 MIN   SERVES 4

1 cup plain fat-free yogurt

1½ tablespoons wasabi

2 teaspoons reduced-sodium soy sauce

2 (6-ounce) cans skinless, boneless pink salmon, drained

½ cup instant potato flakes

½ red bell pepper, finely chopped

2 tablespoons snipped fresh chives

1 Combine ½ cup of the yogurt, 1 tablespoon of the wasabi, and 1 teaspoon of the soy sauce in a bowl. Add the salmon, potato flakes, bell pepper, and chives. Stir the mixture with a large fork until it begins to hold together. With moistened hands, form into 4 (1-inch-thick) patties.

2 To make the sauce, combine the remaining ½ cup yogurt, ½ tablespoon wasabi, and 1 teaspoon soy sauce in a bowl. Set aside.

3 Spray a large nonstick skillet with nonstick spray and set over medium heat. Add the patties and cook until lightly browned and cooked through, about 4 minutes on each side. Serve at once with the sauce and extra snipped chives.

PER SERVING (1 salmon cake with 2 tablespoons sauce): 180 Cal, 4 g Fat, 1 g Sat Fat, 0 g Trans Fat, 71 mg Chol, 499 mg Sod, 12 g Carb, 2 g Fib, 24 g Prot, 365 mg Calc. *POINTS* value: **4.**

TRY IT

Wasabi [WAH-suh-bee], a Japanese version of horseradish, is a green-colored condiment with a pungent, fiery flavor. This recipe uses canned powdered wasabi, which is readily available in the Asian-foods section of most supermarkets.

HALIBUT WITH FENNEL AND TOMATO

PREP 15 MIN   COOK 15 MIN   SERVES 4

- **1 navel orange**
- **1 fennel bulb, trimmed and thinly sliced**
- **2 shallots, thinly sliced**
- **1 (14-ounce) can cherry tomatoes, drained, with ¼ cup of the juice reserved**
- **½ teaspoon salt**
- **4 (5-ounce) skinless halibut or cod fillets**
- **½ teaspoon black pepper**

1 Remove 3 (2-inch) strips of the zest from the orange. Then remove and discard the peel and pith from the orange. Hold the orange over a bowl and cut apart the sections with a small knife.

2 Spray a medium nonstick saucepan with olive oil nonstick spray and set over medium-high heat. Add the fennel, shallots, and orange zest; cook until the fennel is crisp-tender. Stir in the reserved tomato juice. Reduce the heat and cook, covered, until the fennel is just tender. Add the tomatoes, orange sections, and ¼ teaspoon of the salt; cook just until heated through. Cover and keep warm.

3 Sprinkle the fillets with the remaining salt and the pepper. Spray a large nonstick skillet with olive oil nonstick spray and set over medium-high heat. Add the fillets and cook just until opaque in the center, about 4 minutes on each side. Serve with the tomato-fennel mixture.

PER SERVING (1 halibut fillet with ¾ cup fennel-tomato mixture): 190 Cal, 2 g Fat, 0 g Sat Fat, 0 g Trans Fat, 75 mg Chol, 275 mg Sod, 14 g Carb, 4 g Fib, 29 g Prot, 100 mg Calc. **POINTS** value: **3**.

LINGUINE WITH RED CLAM SAUCE

PREP 10 MIN   COOK 20 MIN   SERVES 4

½	**pound whole-wheat linguine**
1	**yellow bell pepper, diced**
1	**onion, diced**
1	**(14½-ounce) can diced tomatoes with garlic and olive oil**
½	**teaspoon crushed red pepper**
1	**(10-ounce) can whole baby clams, with the juice**
¼	**cup chopped fresh flat-leaf parsley**

1 Cook the linguine according to package directions, omitting the salt if desired.

2 Meanwhile, to make the sauce, spray a medium nonstick saucepan with nonstick spray and set over medium-high heat. Add the bell pepper and onion; cook, stirring frequently, until the onion is tender, about 4 minutes. Stir in the tomatoes and crushed red pepper. Reduce the heat and cook, covered, until the flavors are blended, about 12 minutes. Stir in the clams with the clam juice and cook, uncovered, until heated through, about 1 minute longer.

3 Combine the pasta, sauce, and parsley in a large bowl; toss to coat and serve at once.

PER SERVING (1¾ cups): 326 Cal, 3 g Fat, 0 g Sat Fat, 0 g Trans Fat, 36 mg Chol, 409 mg Sod, 55 g Carb, 6 g Fib, 24 g Prot, 120 mg Calc. *POINTS* value: **6.**

ZAP IT

To prepare the sauce, spray a 2-quart microwavable bowl with nonstick spray. Add the bell pepper and onion. Cover the bowl with plastic wrap; prick a few holes in the plastic. Microwave on High 3 minutes. Stir in the tomatoes and crushed red pepper. Microwave, covered, on High 6 minutes. Stir in the clams with the clam juice; cover and keep warm.

SPICY SOUTHWEST-STYLE
MUSSELS

SPICY SOUTHWEST-STYLE MUSSELS

PREP 15 MIN   COOK 15 MIN   SERVES 4

1   **tablespoon extra-virgin olive oil**

3   **garlic cloves, minced**

1   **(12-ounce) can light beer**

1   **(10-ounce) can diced tomatoes and green chiles**

4   **pounds small mussels, scrubbed and debearded**

½   **cup chopped fresh cilantro**

8   **(1-inch-thick) slices French baguette**

1 Heat the oil in a large Dutch oven over medium heat. Add the garlic and cook, stirring frequently, until lightly golden, about 1 minute. Add the beer and bring to a boil. Stir in the tomatoes and green chiles. Add the mussels. Cover and bring to a boil over high heat. Reduce the heat and simmer, covered, until the mussels open, 6–8 minutes.

2 With a slotted spoon, transfer the mussels, tomatoes, and chiles to 4 large bowls. Discard any mussels that have not opened.

3 Stir the cilantro into the broth and ladle the broth over each serving. Serve at once with the bread.

PER SERVING (16 mussels with about ¾ cup broth and 2 slices bread): 250 Cal, 6 g Fat, 1 g Sat Fat, 0 g Trans Fat, 45 mg Chol, 667 mg Sod, 25 g Carb, 2 g Fib, 21 g Prot, 117 mg Calc. *POINTS* value: **5.**

PLAY IT SAFE

The majority of cultivated mussels are clean, but if the broth on the bottom of the pot is sandy when you stir it after the mussels have opened, pour it slowly into a clean saucepan, leaving the sand behind before proceeding to step 2.

CANNELLINI AND CABBAGE SOUP

PREP **5 MIN**   COOK **20 MIN**   SERVES **4**

- **2** teaspoons extra-virgin olive oil
- **1** (1-pound) bag coleslaw mix
- **1** small red onion, chopped
- **2** (14½-ounce) cans chicken broth with roasted vegetables + 14½ ounces (1 can) water
- **1** (15½-ounce) can cannellini beans, rinsed and drained
- **¾** cup whole-wheat elbow macaroni or small shells
- **½** teaspoon black pepper

1 Heat the oil in a nonstick Dutch oven over medium heat. Add the coleslaw mix and the red onion; cook, stirring constantly, until the cabbage is wilted, about 2 minutes. Reduce the heat and cook, covered, stirring, until the onion is tender, about 6 minutes.

2 Add the broth, water, beans, macaroni, and pepper; bring to a boil. Reduce the heat and simmer, covered, until the macaroni is just tender, about 10 minutes. Serve at once.

PER SERVING (2 cups): 276 Cal, 4 g Fat, 1 g Sat Fat, 0 g Trans Fat, 0 mg Chol, 1,134 mg Sod, 46 g Carb, 10 g Fib, 17 g Prot, 145 mg Calc. **POINTS** value: **5.**

GOOD IDEA

Top each serving with ¼ cup shredded fat-free mozzarella cheese if desired (the **POINTS** value will increase by **1**).

HUEVOS RANCHEROS TACOS

PREP 10 MIN   COOK 1 MIN   SERVES 4

1   (14½-ounce) can fire-roasted diced tomatoes, drained

3   tablespoons diced red onion

3   tablespoons chopped fresh cilantro

1   (15½-ounce) can Southwest-style refried black beans with lime juice

8   (6-inch) corn tortillas

2   cups shredded romaine or iceberg lettuce

4   large hard-cooked eggs, peeled and thinly sliced

1 Combine the tomatoes, red onion, and cilantro in a small bowl; set aside. Place the beans in a 1-quart microwavable bowl. Cover with wax paper and microwave on High until hot, 1–2 minutes.

2 Warm the tortillas according to package directions.

3 Spread 3 tablespoons of the beans on half of each tortilla. Top each portion of beans with ¼ cup of the lettuce, slices of half an egg, and 2 tablespoons of the tomato-onion mixture. Fold each tortilla in half and serve at once.

PER SERVING (2 tacos): 306 Cal, 8 g Fat, 2 g Sat Fat, 0 g Trans Fat, 221 mg Chol, 513 mg Sod, 44 g Carb, 10 g Fib, 16 g Prot, 136 mg Calc. *POINTS* value: **6.**

FOOD NOTE

These tacos are also delicious if you substitute baby spinach or arugula for the lettuce.

3

SMART-START MEATS

So many choices from the meat or deli case
means dinner on the double tonight

MIXED-GRILL BROCHETTES

PREP 15 MIN   COOK 10 MIN   SERVES 4

1   pound herb-seasoned beef tenderloin, trimmed and cut into 1½-inch pieces

3   ears corn-on-the-cob, cut crosswise into 3-inch pieces

2   zucchini, cut into 1½-inch pieces

2   plum tomatoes, cut into quarters

1½   teaspoons ground cumin

½   teaspoon salt

1 Spray the broiler rack with nonstick spray and preheat the broiler.

2 Thread the beef, corn, zucchini, and tomatoes alternately on 4 (12-inch) metal skewers. Sprinkle the kebabs with the cumin and salt; lightly spray with nonstick spray.

3 Place the kebabs on the broiler rack and broil 4 inches from the heat, turning every 2 minutes, until the zucchini is tender and the beef is cooked as desired, about 10 minutes for medium rare.

PER SERVING (1 kebab): 293 Cal, 10 g Fat, 3 g Sat Fat, 0 g Trans Fat, 49 mg Chol, 412 mg Sod, 23 g Carb, 5 g Fib, 30 g Prot, 31 mg Calc. *POINTS* value: **6.**

HOW WE DID IT

To thread the pieces of corn on the skewers easily, we pierced the tip of the skewer through the center of the cob, gently twisting it as we glided the skewer through.

MIXED-GRILL
BROCHETTES

KOREAN STEAK KEBABS

PREP 10 MIN   COOK 5 MIN   SERVES 4

¼   **cup reduced-sodium soy sauce**

3   **tablespoons balsamic vinegar**

I   **tablespoon minced peeled fresh ginger**

I   **garlic clove, minced**

I   **pound top-round steak, trimmed and sliced for stir-fry**

1 Spray the broiler rack with canola oil nonstick spray and preheat the boiler.

2 Combine the soy sauce, vinegar, ginger, and garlic in a small bowl; set aside.

3 Thread the steak on 8 (10-inch) metal skewers by piercing each strip in several places so that it lies flat. Brush the kebabs with half the soy sauce mixture. Place on the broiler rack and broil 4 inches from the heat 3 minutes. Turn, brush with the remaining soy sauce mixture, and broil until cooked through, about 3 minutes longer.

PER SERVING (2 kebabs): 158 Cal, 4 g Fat, I g Sat Fat, 0 g Trans Fat, 64 mg Chol, 565 mg Sod, 3 g Carb, 0 g Fib, 27 g Prot, 9 mg Calc. *POINTS* value: *3.*

EXPRESS LANE

To save time in step 2, instead of mincing the ginger and the garlic, grate the garlic clove and a 1-inch piece of peeled ginger on the small-holed side of a box grater right into the soy sauce mixture.

SIZZLING STEAK FAJITAS

PREP 15 MIN   COOK 15 MIN   SERVES 4

2   teaspoons canola oil

1   pound peppercorn- and garlic-
     seasoned beef shoulder filet,
     trimmed and cut into thin
     strips

1   red bell pepper, thinly sliced

1   green bell pepper, thinly
     sliced

1   onion, thinly sliced

1   teaspoon Southwest seasoning

4   (8-inch) multigrain tortillas

1 Heat 1 teaspoon of the oil in a large nonstick skillet over medium-high heat. Add the beef and cook, turning occasionally, until browned, about 6 minutes. Transfer to a plate.

2 Heat the remaining 1 teaspoon oil in the skillet over medium heat. Add the bell pepper, onion, and Southwest seasoning; cook, stirring occasionally, until the vegetables are very soft, about 8 minutes. Add the beef and cook, stirring occasionally, until heated through, about 1 minute.

3 Meanwhile, warm the tortillas according to package directions. Top each tortilla with about 1 cup of the beef mixture. Roll up and serve at once.

PER SERVING (1 fajita): 306 Cal, 11 g Fat, 4 g Sat Fat, 1 g Trans Fat, 64 mg Chol, 791 mg Sod, 26 g Carb, 4 g Fib, 26 g Prot, 50 mg Calc. *POINTS* value: **6.**

FOOD NOTE

If you like your fajitas on the spicy side, substitute a poblano pepper for the green bell pepper in the beef mixture.

CRUNCHY ASIAN BEEF SLAW

PREP 5 MIN   COOK NONE   SERVES 4

3	tablespoons seasoned rice vinegar
1	tablespoon reduced-sodium soy sauce
1	tablespoon packed brown sugar
2	(8- or 10-ounce) bags shredded red cabbage
¼	cup chopped fresh mint
1	(8-ounce) container deli-sliced roast beef, cut into strips
2	tablespoons unsalted dry-roasted peanuts

1 To make the dressing, combine the vinegar, soy sauce, and brown sugar in a small bowl.

2 Combine the cabbage and mint in a large bowl. Add half the dressing and toss to coat. Top with the beef and drizzle with the remaining dressing. Sprinkle with the peanuts and serve at once.

PER SERVING (1½ cups): 159 Cal, 4 g Fat, 1 g Sat Fat, 0 g Trans Fat, 28 mg Chol, 927 mg Sod, 18 g Carb, 3 g Fib, 14 g Prot, 63 mg Calc. *POINTS* value: **3**.

MAKE IT CORE

If you're following the **Core Plan**, prepare the recipe as directed, but use plain rice vinegar in the dressing and skip the peanuts (you'll also reduce the per-serving **POINTS** value by **1**).

CHOUCROUTE À LA MINUTE

PREP **5 MIN**   COOK **25 MIN**   SERVES **4**

2	**cups reduced-sodium sauerkraut, rinsed and drained**
I	**onion, chopped**
½	**cup dry white wine or reduced-sodium chicken broth**
I	**teaspoon caraway seeds**
2	**(¼-pound) fully cooked smoked boneless pork chops, trimmed and cut into 2-inch pieces**
¼	**pound reduced-fat turkey kielbasa, cut into I½-inch slices**

1 Combine the sauerkraut, onion, wine, ½ cup water, and the caraway seeds in a Dutch oven; bring to a boil.

2 Add the pork and kielbasa; simmer, covered, until the pork and kielbasa are heated through and the flavors are blended, about 20 minutes.

PER SERVING (about I cup): 147 Cal, 6 g Fat, 2 g Sat Fat, 0 g Trans Fat, 35 mg Chol, 1,352 mg Sod, 9 g Carb, 4 g Fib, 14 g Prot, 54 mg Calc. *POINTS* value: *3.*

GOOD IDEA

Serve this comfort food classic with steamed baby red potatoes (4 cups cooked potatoes will increase the per-serving *POINTS* value by **2**).

**PEPPERED PORK WITH
FENNEL AND APPLES**

PEPPERED PORK WITH FENNEL AND APPLES

PREP 10 MIN   COOK 20 MIN   SERVES 4

1   (1¼-pound) pepper-seasoned pork tenderloin, trimmed and cut crosswise into 8 (1½-inch-thick) pieces

1   teaspoon canola oil

1   small fennel bulb, trimmed and thinly sliced

1   Granny Smith apple, thinly sliced

¼   cup unsweetened apple juice

2   tablespoons all-fruit apricot spread

1   teaspoon chopped fresh thyme

1 Spray a large nonstick skillet with nonstick spray and set over medium-high heat. Add the pork and cook, turning occasionally, until browned on all sides, about 8 minutes. Transfer to a plate.

2 Heat the oil in the skillet over medium-high heat. Add the fennel and apple; cook, stirring occasionally, just until tender, about 5 minutes. Stir in the apple juice, apricot spread, thyme, and the pork, along with any accumulated juices. Bring the mixture just to a boil. Reduce the heat and simmer, covered, until the pork is cooked through, about 6 minutes longer. Serve at once.

PER SERVING (2 pieces pork with generous ⅓ cup apple mixture): 252 Cal, 7 g Fat, 2 g Sat Fat, 0 g Trans Fat, 84 mg Chol, 269 mg Sod, 17 g Carb, 3 g Fib, 31 g Prot, 43 mg Calc. *POINTS* value: **5.**

HOW WE DID IT

Our fennel bulbs had feathery fronds and thick stalks attached. We cut them off (and saved them to make stock). We cut about ¼ inch off the bottom of each bulb, removed the core, and then sliced the bulb.

GRILLED HAM STEAK WITH PINEAPPLE SALSA

PREP 10 MIN   COOK 10 MIN   SERVES 4

- **2   cups peeled, cored, and diced fresh pineapple**
- **2   tablespoons chopped fresh mint**
- **1   tablespoon minced peeled fresh ginger**
- **1   tablespoon lime juice**
- **1   jalapeño pepper, seeded and minced (wear gloves to prevent irritation)**
- **1   (1-pound) fully cooked boneless reduced-sodium lean ham steak, ½ inch thick**

1 To make the salsa, combine the pineapple, mint, ginger, lime juice, and jalapeño in a medium bowl; set aside.

2 Spray a nonstick ridged grill pan or medium nonstick skillet with canola oil nonstick spray and set over medium-high heat. Add the ham steak and cook until browned and heated through, about 4 minutes on each side. Cut into quarters and serve with the salsa.

PER SERVING (¼ ham steak with ½ cup salsa): 190 Cal, 6 g Fat, 2 g Sat Fat, 0 g Trans Fat, 53 mg Chol, 980 mg Sod, 13 g Carb, 1 g Fib, 22 g Prot, 22 mg Calc. **POINTS** value: **4.**

FOOD NOTE

Peeled, cored, and diced fresh pineapple can be found in the produce section of most supermarkets. But you may also use a 20-ounce can of pineapple chunks in juice, drained and coarsely chopped.

FRENCH-BREAD PIZZAS WITH PROSCIUTTO

PREP 10 MIN   COOK 5 MIN   SERVES 4

1	(8-ounce) loaf whole-wheat French bread, split
2	tablespoons prepared pesto
6	thin slices prosciutto (about 3 ounces), trimmed
2	plum tomatoes, cut into thin wedges
½	cup shredded part-skim mozzarella cheese
2	tablespoons chopped fresh basil

1 Preheat the broiler.

2 Pull out some of the bread from the center of each piece of the French bread and discard. Place the bread shells, cut side up, on the broiler rack. Spread each piece with 1 tablespoon of the pesto. Top each one with 3 slices of the prosciutto, half the tomatoes, and ¼ cup of the cheese.

3 Broil the pizzas 6 inches from the heat until the topping is hot and the cheese is melted, about 6 minutes. Sprinkle each one with ½ tablespoon of the basil and cut crosswise in half, making a total of 4 pizzas. Serve at once.

PER SERVING (1 pizza): 208 Cal, 10 g Fat, 3 g Sat Fat, 0 g Trans Fat, 20 mg Chol, 597 mg Sod, 18 g Carb, 3 g Fib, 12 g Prot, 161 mg Calc. *POINTS* value: *4.*

GOOD IDEA

Making your own pesto is a snap. Puree 2 cups packed fresh basil leaves, 2 tablespoons pine nuts, 2 tablespoons grated Parmesan cheese, 2 tablespoons water, 5 teaspoons extra-virgin olive oil, and 1 chopped garlic clove in a blender or food processor. This recipe makes about ½ cup. Per-serving (1 tablespoon) has a *POINTS* value of *1.*

OPEN-FACE PITA CALZONES

PREP 10 MIN   COOK 5 MIN   SERVES 4

½ **cup part-skim ricotta cheese**

2 **tablespoons chopped fresh parsley**

1 **teaspoon chopped fresh thyme**

2 **(6-inch) whole-wheat pitas, split horizontally**

2 **ounces fully cooked lean ham, chopped**

2 **ounces sliced cooked turkey breast, chopped**

½ **cup shredded reduced-fat Italian cheese blend**

1 Preheat the broiler.

2 Combine the ricotta, parsley, and thyme in a small bowl. Place the pitas, cut side up, on the broiler rack. Spread each piece with 2 tablespoons of the ricotta mixture almost to the edge. Top each one with one quarter of the ham, one quarter of the turkey, and 2 tablespoons of the cheese blend.

3 Broil 4 inches from the heat until the topping is hot and the cheese blend is melted, about 6 minutes. Serve at once.

PER SERVING (1 calzone): 192 Cal, 7 g Fat, 4 g Sat Fat, 0 g Trans Fat, 37 mg Chol, 433 mg Sod, 17 g Carb, 2 g Fib, 16 g Prot, 180 mg Calc. **POINTS** value: **4**.

TRY IT

To make quesadillas, layer one quarter of the ricotta mixture, ham, turkey, and cheese blend on half of each of 4 (7-inch) whole-wheat tortillas. Fold the unfilled half of each tortilla over the filling. Spray a large nonstick skillet with nonstick spray and set over medium heat. Add the quesadillas and cook until the filling is hot, 3 minutes on each side.

CHICKEN PROVENÇAL

PREP 10 MIN   COOK 10 MIN   SERVES 4

- 4 **(5-ounce) skinless, boneless chicken breasts**
- ½ **cup reduced-sodium chicken broth**
- 2 **plum tomatoes, chopped**
- 1 **red onion, thinly sliced**
- 8 **brine-cured pitted kalamata olives, chopped**
- 3 **tablespoons chopped fresh basil**

1 Spray a large nonstick skillet with olive oil nonstick spray and set over medium-high heat. Add the chicken and cook until lightly browned, about 3 minutes on each side.

2 Add the broth, tomatoes, red onion, and olives; bring to a boil. Reduce the heat and simmer, covered, until the vegetables are tender and the chicken is cooked through, about 5 minutes. Remove the skillet from the heat; stir in the basil and serve at once.

PER SERVING (1 chicken breast with ¼ cup sauce): 202 Cal, 5 g Fat, 1 g Sat Fat, 0 g Trans Fat, 86 mg Chol, 219 mg Sod, 5 g Carb, 1 g Fib, 32 g Prot, 36 mg Calc. *POINTS* value: *4.*

FOOD NOTE

Look for kalamata olives at the supermarket's salad bar. Other good choices include brine-cured gaeta and green olives.

CHICKEN SALTIMBOCCA

PREP 10 MIN   COOK 10 MIN   SERVES 4

4   (¼-pound) chicken cutlets

2   (½-ounce) slices fully cooked lean ham, cut in half

2   (½-ounce) slices fat-free Swiss cheese, cut in half

8   large fresh basil leaves

1   large lemon

1   cup reduced-sodium chicken broth

1 Arrange the chicken breasts on a work surface with the short sides near you. Top each one with 1 slice of the ham, 1 slice of the cheese, and 2 basil leaves. Roll up, jelly-roll-style, and secure with a wooden pick.

2 Grate 1 tablespoon of the zest from the lemon; squeeze 1 tablespoon of juice.

3 Spray a large nonstick skillet with olive oil nonstick spray and set over medium-high heat. Add the chicken rolls, seam side down, and cook until lightly browned, about 2 minutes on each side. Add the broth, lemon zest, and lemon juice; bring to a boil. Reduce the heat and simmer, covered, just until the chicken is cooked through, about 8 minutes.

PER SERVING (1 chicken roll with ¼ cup sauce): 167 Cal, 4 g Fat, 1 g Sat Fat, 0 g Trans Fat, 72 mg Chol, 371 mg Sod, 2 g Carb, 0 g Fib, 29 g Prot, 72 mg Calc. **POINTS** value: **4.**

FOOD NOTE

Substitute fresh sage leaves for the basil if desired.

CHIPOTLE CHICKEN QUESADILLAS

PREP 10 MIN   COOK 10 MIN   SERVES 4

4   (6- or 8-inch) fat-free flour tortillas

½   cup shredded reduced-fat Mexican cheese blend

½   cup shredded romaine lettuce

2   cups chopped sliced deli-roasted chicken breast

½   cup salsa

4   tablespoons chopped fresh cilantro

Chipotle pepper sauce

1 Place the tortillas on a work surface; sprinkle the cheese and lettuce evenly over half of each tortilla. Top each one with ½ cup of the chicken, 2 tablespoons of the salsa, 1 tablespoon of the cilantro, and a dash of the pepper sauce. Fold the unfilled half of each tortilla over the filling.

2 Spray a large nonstick skillet with nonstick spray and set over medium-high heat. Place 2 tortillas in the skillet. Cook until crisp on the bottom, 2–3 minutes. Spray the tops with nonstick spray and turn them over. Cook until crisp on the bottom, 1–2 minutes. Transfer the quesadillas to a cutting board, cover loosely with foil, and set aside.

3 Cook the remaining 2 quesadillas. Cut each quesadilla in half and serve at once.

PER SERVING (1 quesadilla): 216 Cal, 5 g Fat, 2 g Sat Fat, 0 g Trans Fat, 60 mg Chol, 787 mg Sod, 16 g Carb, 3 g Fib, 27 g Prot, 171 mg Calc. *POINTS* value: *4.*

FOOD NOTE

If you prefer your quesadillas less spicy, skip the chipotle pepper sauce or use mild cayenne pepper sauce instead.

CHICKEN WITH ANDOUILLE AND PEPPERS

PREP 10 MIN   COOK 15 MIN   SERVES 4

- ½ **pound chicken tenders, cut into 1½-inch pieces**
- ¼ **pound andouille or other spicy smoked sausage, cut on the diagonal into 1½-inch slices**
- 1 **onion, thinly sliced**
- 1 **red bell pepper, thinly sliced**
- ½ **teaspoon Cajun seasoning, optional**
- 1 **(14½-ounce) can diced tomatoes**

1 Spray a large nonstick skillet with nonstick spray and set over medium-high heat. Add the chicken and cook, stirring occasionally, until browned, 2–3 minutes; transfer to a plate. Add the sausage to the skillet and cook, stirring occasionally, until browned, 3–4 minutes. Drain on paper towels.

2 Wipe the skillet with paper towels; spray with nonstick spray and set over medium heat. Add the onion, bell pepper, and Cajun seasoning (if using); cook, stirring occasionally, until the vegetables are tender, about 5 minutes. Add the tomatoes and bring to a boil. Add the chicken and sausage; return to a boil. Reduce the heat and simmer, covered, until the chicken is cooked through, 6–8 minutes longer.

PER SERVING (generous 1 cup): 203 Cal, 10 g Fat, 3 g Sat Fat, 0 g Trans Fat, 58 mg Chol, 445 mg Sod, 9 g Carb, 2 g Fib, 19 g Prot, 50 mg Calc. *POINTS* value: 4.

GOOD IDEA

Serve this Louisiana specialty with a side of hearty brown rice (½ cup cooked rice for each serving will increase the *POINTS* value by 2).

BARBECUE CHICKEN SANDWICHES

PREP 5 MIN   COOK 5 MIN   SERVES 4

1 (10-ounce) package sliced honey-roasted grilled chicken breast

1 cup barbecue sauce

2 tablespoons apple-cider vinegar

1 teaspoon mild cayenne pepper sauce

4 whole-wheat hamburger buns

1 cup coleslaw mix

1 Combine the chicken, barbecue sauce, vinegar, and pepper sauce in a medium saucepan. Cook, covered, over medium heat, stirring occasionally, until heated through, about 5 minutes.

2 Slice the buns horizontally almost all the way through; spread open. Place ½ cup of the chicken mixture and then ¼ cup of the coleslaw mix on the bottom of each bun. Close the buns and serve at once.

PER SERVING (I sandwich): 336 Cal, 5 g Fat, I g Sat Fat, 0 g Trans Fat, 60 mg Chol, 1,036 mg Sod, 47 g Carb, 4 g Fib, 27 g Prot, 84 mg Calc. *POINTS* value: **6.**

FOOD NOTE

This classic sandwich is also tasty on a kaiser roll, although you may want to pull out some of the bread from the center after cutting the rolls open in step 2. A 2-ounce kaiser roll willl increase the **POINTS** value by **2.**

HONEY-GLAZED TURKEY WITH SWEET POTATOES

PREP 10 MIN   COOK 20 MIN   SERVES 4

½ **cup orange juice**

¼ **cup reduced-sodium chicken broth**

1 **tablespoon honey**

2 **teaspoons Dijon mustard**

1 **teaspoon chopped fresh thyme**

1 **(1-pound) turkey tenderloin**

1 **pound sweet potatoes, peeled and cut into 1-inch pieces**

1 Combine the orange juice, broth, honey, mustard, and thyme in a small bowl, beating with a whisk until blended. Set aside.

2 Spray a nonstick Dutch oven with nonstick spray and set over medium-high heat. Add the turkey and cook, turning occasionally, until browned, about 3 minutes. Add the sweet potatoes and the orange juice mixture; bring to a boil. Reduce the heat and simmer, covered, until the turkey is cooked through and the sweet potatoes are fork-tender, about 15 minutes.

3 Transfer the turkey to a cutting board and cut into 8 slices. Serve with the sweet potatoes and the sauce.

PER SERVING (2 slices turkey with ½ cup potatoes and 1 tablespoon sauce): 222 Cal, 1 g Fat, 0 g Sat Fat, 0 g Trans Fat, 75 mg Chol, 171 mg Sod, 23 g Carb, 2 g Fib, 28 g Prot, 43 mg Calc. *POINTS* value: **4.**

EXPRESS LANE

Skip the honey and the mustard and use 1 tablespoon honey mustard instead.

CHICKEN AND EGGPLANT ROULADES

PREP 10 MIN   COOK 10 MIN   SERVES 4

- 1 (1-pound) eggplant, cut lengthwise into 8 slices
- ½ cup crumbled fat-free feta cheese
- 4 canned water-packed artichoke hearts, drained and chopped
- 4 tablespoons thinly sliced fresh basil
- 1 (10-ounce) package sliced grilled chicken breast
- 1 cup Italian-style tomato sauce

1 Spray the broiler rack with olive oil nonstick spray and preheat the broiler. Place the eggplant in one layer on the broiler rack and lightly spray with olive oil nonstick spray. Broil 6 inches from the heat until lightly browned, about 4 minutes. Place the eggplant, broiled side down, on a work surface and let cool.

2 Meanwhile, combine the cheese, artichoke hearts, and 2 tablespoons of the basil in a small bowl.

3 Place ¼ cup of the chicken onto one short end of each eggplant slice. Top each portion of chicken with about 2 tablespoons of the cheese mixture and roll up. Place the roulades, seam side down, in a shallow 1-quart microwavable dish. Top with the tomato sauce and the remaining basil. Cover with plastic wrap; then prick a few holes in the plastic. Microwave on High 4 minutes. Uncover and microwave until heated through and bubbly, 3–4 minutes longer.

PER SERVING (2 roulades with ¼ cup sauce): 219 Cal, 4 g Fat, 1 g Sat Fat, 0 g Trans Fat, 65 mg Chol, 740 mg Sod, 19 g Carb, 5 g Fib, 27 g Prot, 105 mg Calc. *POINTS* value: 4.

MEDITERRANEAN MEATBALL PITAS

PREP 10 MIN   COOK 5 MIN   SERVES 4

½   cup plain fat-free Greek-style yogurt

1   tablespoon lemon juice

1   tablespoon chopped fresh mint

1   (12-ounce) package fully cooked turkey meatballs

4   (6-inch) multigrain pitas

1   tomato, chopped

½   cucumber, peeled, seeded, and diced

Fresh mint leaves, optional

1 Combine the yogurt, lemon juice, and chopped mint in a small bowl; set aside.

2 Spray a large nonstick skillet with nonstick spray and set over medium heat. Add the meatballs and cook, covered, turning frequently, until heated through, about 5 minutes.

3 Cut a pocket in each pita. Fill each pocket with 3 meatballs, about 2 tablespoons of the tomato, about 2 tablespoons of the cucumber, about 2 tablespoons of the yogurt mixture, and mint leaves (if using). Serve at once.

PER SERVING (1 sandwich): 353 Cal, 9 g Fat, 2 g Sat Fat, 0 g Trans Fat, 90 mg Chol, 787 mg Sod, 43 g Carb, 4 g Fib, 26 g Prot, 144 mg Calc. *POINTS* value: **7.**

ZAP IT

If you prefer the pitas warmed, stack them on a microwavable plate. Cover with a sheet of wax paper or paper towel and microwave on High until heated through, 10–15 seconds.

MEDITERRANEAN
MEATBALL PITAS

TAKE A JAR OF...

Discover the tasty meals you can make with
a jar and a twist of the wrist

BALSAMIC STEAK WITH PEPPER SAUCE

PREP 15 MIN   **COOK** 15 MIN   **SERVES** 4

- **1   (1¼-pound) flank steak, trimmed**
- **⅓ + ½ cup balsamic vinegar**
- **1½ tablespoons ketchup**
- **1   (7-ounce) jar roasted red peppers (not packed in oil), drained and coarsely chopped**
- **½   cup jarred sliced hot cherry peppers, seeded and coarsely chopped**
- **½   cup fresh basil leaves, chopped**
- **2   scallions, sliced**

1 To marinate the steak, put the it in a zip-close plastic bag; add ⅓ cup of the vinegar. Squeeze out the air and seal the bag; turn to coat the steak . Let stand 15 minutes at room temperature, turning the bag occasionally.

2 Meanwhile, combine the remaining ½ cup vinegar and the ketchup in a small saucepan. Cook over medium heat, stirring occasionally, until the mixture comes to a simmer, 1–2 minutes. Reduce the heat and cook until the mixture is syrupy and reduced to ¼ cup, 3–4 minutes. Transfer to a medium bowl and stir in the remaining ingredients.

3 Remove the steak from the marinade; discard the marinade. Pat the steak dry and spray with olive oil nonstick spray. Heat a ridged grill pan over medium-high heat. Add the steak and cook until an instant-read thermometer inserted into the side registers 145°F for medium, 5–6 minutes on each side. Cut into 12 slices and serve with the sauce.

PER SERVING (3 slices steak with ½ cup sauce): 262 Cal, 10 g Fat, 4 g Sat Fat, 0 g Trans Fat, 62 mg Chol, 206 mg Sod, 7 g Carb, 1 g Fib, 34 g Prot, 31 mg Calc. **POINTS** value: **6.**

SPEEDY BEEF BORSCHT

PREP 5 MIN   COOK 15 MIN   SERVES 4

- 1 (14½-ounce) can Italian-style stewed tomatoes, chopped, with the juice
- 1 (14½-ounce) can reduced-sodium beef broth
- 1 (16-ounce) jar pickled beets, drained, with the liquid reserved
- ½ small green cabbage, sliced (about 2½ cups)
- 4 scallions, chopped
- ½ teaspoon dried dill
- ¼ pound deli-sliced roast beef

1 Combine the tomatoes, tomato juice, broth, beet liquid, cabbage, scallions, and dill in a medium saucepan ; bring to a simmer over medium heat. Cook, stirring occasionally, until the cabbage is tender, about 10 minutes.

2 Meanwhile, chop the beets and roast beef. Add to the cabbage mixture; cook, stirring occasionally, just until heated through, about 2 minutes.

PER SERVING (1½ cups): 142 Cal, 2 g Fat, 1 g Sat Fat, 0 g Trans Fat, 14 mg Chol, 767 mg Sod, 23 g Carb, 4 g Fib, 10 g Prot, 84 mg Calc. *POINTS* value: *2*.

HOW WE DID IT

To prep the canned tomatoes without losing any of the juice, we used kitchen shears and chopped the tomatoes while they were still in the can.

ASIAN CHICKEN-LETTUCE WRAPS

1 pound chicken tenders, cut crosswise into 1-inch pieces

1 (10-ounce) bag shredded carrots

⅓ cup jarred chili-garlic sauce

1 bunch scallions, chopped

½ cup fresh cilantro leaves, coarsely chopped

8 large Boston lettuce leaves

8 lime wedges

1 To make the filling, spray a large nonstick skillet with nonstick spray and set over medium-high heat. Add the chicken and carrots; cook, stirring occasionally, until the chicken is cooked through, 5–6 minutes. Stir in the chili sauce and scallions; cook, stirring frequently, until heated through, about 1 minute. Remove the skillet from the heat and stir in the cilantro.

2 Place 2 lettuce leaves on each of 4 plates. Place ½ cup filling on each leaf, squeeze the juice from 1 lime wedge over the top of each one, and roll up. Serve at once.

PER SERVING (2 wraps): 213 Cal, 4 g Fat, 1 g Sat Fat, 0 g Trans Fat, 68 mg Chol, 421 mg Sod, 16 g Carb, 5 g Fib, 27 g Prot, 84 mg Calc. *POINTS* value: **4.**

TRY IT

Chinese chili-garlic sauce is made from hot peppers, garlic, rice vinegar, and salt. Look for jars of it in Asian grocery stores or in the Asian-foods section of the supermarket.

ASIAN CHICKEN-LETTUCE WRAPS

TAPENADE-STUFFED CHICKEN BREASTS

PREP 10 MIN COOK 15 MIN SERVES 4

½ cup crumbled fat-free goat cheese

1 tablespoon jarred tapenade

1½ teaspoons chopped fresh thyme

4 (5-ounce) skinless, boneless chicken breasts

1 teaspoon olive oil

1 To make the stuffing, combine the cheese, tapenade, and thyme in a small bowl.

2 Make a pocket in the side of each chicken breast by inserting a sharp paring knife into the thickest part and gently cutting back and forth until a small chamber opens in the side; do not cut all the way through the breast. Enlarge the pockets gently with your fingers. Stuff 1½ tablespoons stuffing into each breast. Close the pockets with toothpicks.

3 Heat the oil in a large nonstick skillet over medium heat. Add the breasts and cook until browned and cooked through, 6–7 minutes on each side. Remove the toothpicks and serve at once.

PER SERVING (1 stuffed chicken breast): 234 Cal, 10 g Fat, 4 g Sat Fat, 0 g Trans Fat, 94 mg Chol, 184 mg Sod, 0 g Carb, 0 g Fib, 34 g Prot, 42 mg Calc. *POINTS* value: **6.**

TRY IT

Tapenade (tah-puh-NAHD) is a French-style olive paste that includes capers, garlic, and herbs. In a pinch, you can substitute an equal amount of finely chopped brine-cured kalamata olives—and make it a **Core Plan** recipe to boot. The *POINTS* value will remain the same.

CHICKEN ARRABIATA

PREP 15 MIN   COOK 10 MIN   SERVES 4

1⅔ cups jarred tomato and basil sauce (without added sugar)

1 small garlic clove, finely chopped

¼ teaspoon crushed red pepper

6 jarred pitted kalamata olives, drained and chopped

4 (5-ounce) skinless, boneless chicken breasts, pounded to a ½-inch thickness

¼ teaspoon salt

½ cup fresh basil leaves, chopped

1 Combine the tomato sauce, garlic, crushed red pepper, and olives in a small saucepan; bring to a simmer over medium heat. Reduce the heat and cook, covered, until the flavors are blended, about 8 minutes.

2 Meanwhile, sprinkle the chicken with the salt and spray with nonstick spray. Heat a ridged grill pan over medium-high heat. Add the chicken and cook until browned and cooked through, 4–5 minutes on each side.

3 Transfer to a platter. Stir ¼ cup of the basil into the sauce. Top the chicken with the sauce and the remaining ¼ cup basil. Serve at once.

PER SERVING (1 chicken breast with about 6 tablespoons sauce): 234 Cal, 6 g Fat, 1 g Sat Fat, 0 g Trans Fat, 86 mg Chol, 554 mg Sod, 9 g Carb, 2 g Fib, 33 g Prot, 44 mg Calc. *POINTS* value: **5.**

HOW WE DID IT

To prep the chicken breasts in a snap, we placed each breast between 2 sheets of plastic wrap (you can also use wax paper) and lightly pounded them with a meat mallet (you can also use a heavy saucepan).

TURKEY REUBENS

TURKEY REUBENS

PREP 10 MIN   COOK 5 MIN   SERVES 4

¼   cup reduced-fat Thousand Island dressing

1   tablespoon drained jarred capers, chopped

8   slices reduced-calorie seedless rye bread

6   ounces sliced turkey pastrami

½   cup jarred pickled red cabbage, squeezed dry

4   (¾-ounce) slices reduced-fat Swiss cheese

1 Combine the dressing and capers in a small bowl; spread over 4 slices of the bread. Top each slice with one quarter of the pastrami, one quarter of the cabbage, and 1 slice of cheese. Cover the sandwiches with the remaining slices of bread.

2 Spray a large nonstick skillet or griddle with nonstick spray and set over medium-low heat. Add the sandwiches (in batches if necessary) and cook until the bread is toasted and the cheese is melted, about 2 minutes on each side. Cut each sandwich in half and serve at once.

PER SERVING (1 sandwich): 251 Cal, 5 g Fat, 2 g Sat Fat, 0 g Trans Fat, 36 mg Chol, 894 mg Sod, 37 g Carb, 6 g Fib, 18 g Prot, 261 mg Calc. *POINTS* value: *5.*

GOOD IDEA

These sandwiches make excellent panini. Prepare as directed in step 1. Then heat a panini sandwich maker according to the manufacturer's directions. Add the sandwiches and cook about 2 minutes.

BUFFALO CHICKEN BURGERS

PREP 10 MIN   COOK 10 MIN   SERVES 4

1   **pound ground skinless chicken breast**

1   **large celery stalk, chopped**

2   **scallions, chopped**

3   **tablespoons quick-cooking oats**

3-4 **tablespoons mild cayenne pepper sauce**

3   **tablespoons jarred reduced-fat blue cheese dressing**

1 Combine the chicken, celery, scallions, oats, and 2 tablespoons of the pepper sauce in a medium bowl. Form the mixture into 4 (½-inch-thick) patties.

2 Spray a ridged grill pan with nonstick spray and set over medium heat. Add the patties and cook until an instant-read thermometer inserted into the side of each one registers 165°F, about 5 minutes on each side. Drizzle each burger with the dressing and the remaining 1–2 tablespoons pepper sauce.

PER SERVING (1 burger with about 2 teaspoons dressing and 1½ teaspoons pepper sauce): 171 Cal, 5 g Fat, 1 g Sat Fat, 0 g Trans Fat, 69 mg Chol, 495 mg Sod, 4 g Carb, 1 g Fib, 26 g Prot, 37 mg Calc. *POINTS* value: *4.*

MAKE IT CORE

It's easy to enjoy these burgers on the **Core Plan.** Just spray the grill pan with canola or olive oil nonstick spray and use fat-free blue cheese dressing (the *POINTS* value will remain the same).

TILAPIA ESCABÈCHE

PREP 10 MIN   COOK 15 MIN   SERVES 4

2   lemons

4   (¼-pound) skinless tilapia fillets

2   different-colored bell peppers, cut into 2-inch strips

3   garlic cloves, cut into thin slivers

1   (16-ounce) jar fat-free salsa

¾   cup orange juice

¾   teaspoon honey

1 Grate 1 teaspoon of the zest from 1 lemon and squeeze 2 tablespoons of juice. Cut the remaining lemon into 4 wedges. Set aside.

2 Spray a large nonstick skillet with nonstick spray and set over medium heat. Add the fillets and cook just until opaque in the center, 2–3 minutes on each side. Transfer to a plate.

3 Add the bell peppers and garlic to the skillet; cook, stirring frequently, until the bell peppers are crisp-tender, about 5 minutes. Stir in the salsa, orange juice, honey, and the reserved lemon zest and juice; bring to simmer. Cook, stirring occasionally, until the bell peppers are just tender, about 5 minutes. Add the fillets and spoon the vegetables and sauce over the top. Cook until the fillets are heated through, about 2 minutes longer. Serve at once with the lemon wedges.

PER SERVING (1 fillet with ⅔ cup sauce and 1 lemon wedge): 181 Cal, 2 g Fat, 0 g Sat Fat, 0 g Trans Fat, 60 mg Chol, 778 mg Sod, 19 g Carb, 3 g Fib, 24 g Prot, 64 mg Calc. *POINTS* value: *3.*

DUCK WITH PORT AND FIG GLAZE

PREP 5 MIN   **COOK** 15 MIN   **SERVES** 4

1 teaspoon olive oil

4 (5-ounce) skinless, boneless duck breasts

2 shallots, finely chopped

1½ teaspoons chopped fresh rosemary

⅓ cup port or grape juice

¼ cup jarred fig or blackberry jam

⅛ teaspoon salt

Roasted Butternut Squash, page 32, optional

1 Heat the oil in a large nonstick skillet over medium-low heat. Add the duck, skinned side down, and cook until golden, about 5 minutes. Turn, sprinkle the shallots around the breasts, and cook just until the duck is cooked through, about 5 minutes. With tongs, transfer the duck to a plate and keep warm. Leave the shallots in the skillet.

2 To make the glaze, add the rosemary to the skillet and cook, stirring frequently, until fragrant, about 30 seconds. Stir in the port, jam, and any juices that have accumulated from the duck; increase the heat and bring to a simmer. Cook, stirring occasionally, until the mixture is reduced to ½ cup, about 2 minutes. Stir in the salt.

3 Drizzle the duck evenly with the glaze and serve at once with the squash (if using).

PER SERVING (1 duck breast with 2 tablespoons glaze and without squash): 223 Cal, 2 g Fat, 1 g Sat Fat, 0 g Trans Fat, 83 mg Chol, 134 mg Sod, 18 g Carb, 1 g Fib, 30 g Prot, 26 mg Calc. *POINTS* value: *4*.

DUCK WITH PORT
AND FIG GLAZE
WITH ROASTED
BUTTERNUT SQUASH

GRILLED TUNA AND ARTICHOKE SALAD

PREP 15 MIN   COOK 5 MIN   SERVES 4

1	pound ½-inch thick tuna steak
8	tablespoons fat-free Italian dressing
3	(4-ounce) bags mixed baby greens
2	(14-ounce) cans water-packed artichokes, drained and quartered
1	(7-ounce) jar roasted red peppers (not packed in oil), drained and sliced
½	cup drained canned chickpeas
4	lemon wedges

1 Brush the tuna with 2 tablespoons of the dressing. Spray a ridged grill pan with canola oil nonstick spray and set over medium heat. Add the tuna and cook until browned and pink in the center, 2–3 minutes on each side. Transfer to a cutting board and let cool slightly about 5 minutes.

2 Meanwhile, divide the greens among 4 plates.

3 Cut the tuna into 12 slices. Top each plate with 3 slices of the tuna, one quarter of the artichokes, ¼ cup of the roasted peppers, and 2 tablespoons of the chickpeas. Drizzle the salads evenly with the remaining 6 tablespoons dressing. Serve at once with the lemon wedges.

PER SERVING (3½ cups salad with 1½ tablespoons dressing and 1 lemon wedge): 279 Cal, 7 g Fat, 2 g Sat Fat, 0 g Trans Fat, 67 mg Chol, 647 mg Sod, 28 g Carb, 12 g Fib, 30 g Prot, 135 mg Calc. *POINTS* value: *5.*

EXPRESS LANE

Instead of cooking fresh tuna in step 1, top the salads with 2 (6-ounce) cans drained chunk white tuna in water (you'll also reduce the per-serving *POINTS* value by *1*).

FISH TACOS

PREP 15 MIN   COOK 10 MIN   SERVES 4

1 pound skinless grouper fillets, cut crosswise into ¾-inch strips

4 tablespoons jarred reduced-fat mayonnaise

½ cup cornmeal

2 tablespoons seasoned rice-wine vinegar

4 tablespoons chopped fresh cilantro

4 (8-inch) whole-wheat tortillas

2 cups shredded green cabbage

1 Preheat the oven to 425°F. Line a baking sheet with foil and spray the foil with nonstick spray.

2 Combine the grouper and 1 tablespoon of the mayonnaise in a medium bowl. Place the cornmeal on a sheet of wax paper. In small batches, toss the grouper with the cornmeal to coat. Place the grouper on the baking sheet and lightly spray with nonstick spray. Bake until browned and cooked through, 6–7 minutes.

3 Meanwhile, combine the remaining 3 tablespoons mayonnaise, the vinegar, and 2 tablespoons of the cilantro in a medium bowl. Warm the tortillas according to package directions. Spoon one quarter of the grouper along the center of each tortilla. Top each with ½ cup of the cabbage and ½ tablespoon of the remaining cilantro. Fold each tortilla in half and serve at once.

PER SERVING (1 taco): 311 Cal, 8 g Fat, 1 g Sat Fat, 0 g Trans Fat, 65 mg Chol, 528 mg Sod, 34 g Carb, 5 g Fib, 27 g Prot, 60 mg Calc. *POINTS* value: **6.**

SNAPPER WITH TROPICAL FRUIT SALSA

PREP 10 MIN   COOK 10 MIN   SERVES 4

1   large lime

1   cup jarred refrigerated tropical fruit in light syrup, drained, cut into ½-inch pieces, with ½ cup of the syrup reserved

4   (5- to 6-ounce) skinless red snapper fillets

½   red bell pepper, cut into ½-inch strips

½   fennel bulb, trimmed and cut into 1-inch strips

1   teaspoon olive oil

¼   teaspoon salt

1 Grate 1 teaspoon of the zest from the lime; squeeze 2 tablespoons of juice and set aside. Put ⅓ cup of the reserved fruit syrup and the lime zest in a zip-close plastic bag; add the fillets. Squeeze out the air and seal the bag; turn to coat the fillets. Refrigerate, turning the bag occasionally, 15 minutes.

2 Meanwhile, spray the broiler rack with nonstick spray and preheat the broiler. To make the salsa, combine the fruit, bell pepper, fennel, oil, salt, the reserved lime juice, and the remaining fruit syrup in a medium bowl.

3 Drain the fillets; discard the marinade. Place the fillets on the broiler rack and broil 5 inches from the heat just until opaque in the center, about 8 minutes. Serve with the salsa.

PER SERVING (1 fillet with ½ cup salsa): 202 Cal, 3 g Fat, 1 g Sat Fat, 0 g Trans Fat, 75 mg Chol, 284 mg Sod, 16 g Carb, 2 g Fib, 28 g Prot, 40 mg Calc. *POINTS* value: 4.

GOOD IDEA

If your fennel bulb has its feathery fronds attached, by all means use them—they are full of flavor. Just add 2 tablespoons of chopped fronds to the salsa in step 2.

SHRIMP ROMESCO

PREP 10 MIN   **COOK** 5 MIN   **SERVES** 4

1 (12-ounce) jar roasted red peppers with balsamic vinegar, drained well

1 cup Italian-style tomato sauce

2 teaspoons smoked paprika

1 teaspoon olive oil

1 pound large peeled and deveined shrimp

¼ cup thinly sliced fresh basil

1 Puree the peppers, tomato sauce, and paprika in a food processor or blender and set aside.

2 Heat the oil in a large nonstick skillet over medium-high heat. Add the shrimp and cook just until opaque in the center, 1–2 minutes on each side. Transfer to a plate.

3 Add the pepper mixture to the skillet. Reduce the heat and cook, stirring occasionally, until the mixture is slightly thickened and the flavors are blended, about 4 minutes. Add the shrimp and basil; cook, stirring occasionally, until heated through, about 1 minute longer. Serve at once.

PER SERVING (¾ cup): 133 Cal, 2 g Fat, 0 g Sat Fat, 0 g Trans Fat, 161 mg Chol, 639 mg Sod, 10 g Carb, 2 g Fib, 19 g Prot, 52 mg Calc. **POINTS** value: **2.**

GOOD IDEA

Serve this dish over cooked whole-wheat linguine (⅔ cup for each serving will increase the **POINTS** value by **2**).

SHRIMP ROMESCO

SHRIMP CAKES WITH SPICY TARTAR SAUCE

PREP 15 MIN   COOK 5 MIN   SERVES 4

1 pound large peeled and deveined shrimp

1 egg white

1 scallion, sliced

1 tablespoon + 2 teaspoons chopped fresh dill

2 tablespoons canned sliced pickled jalapeño peppers, drained and chopped

⅓ cup panko (Japanese bread crumbs)

5 tablespoons jarred tartar sauce

1 Pulse the shrimp, egg white, scallion, 1 tablespoon of dill, and 1 tablespoon of the jalapeño in a food processor just until coarsely chopped. Add the bread crumbs and 1 tablespoon of the tartar sauce; pulse just until combined. With a ¼-cup dry measure, form the mixture into 8 (½-inch-thick) cakes.

2 To make the sauce, combine the remaining 4 tablespoons tartar sauce, 2 teaspoons dill, and 1 tablespoon jalapeño. Set aside.

3 Spray a large nonstick skillet with nonstick spray and set over medium-low heat. Add the cakes and cook, covered, until opaque throughout, about 2½ minutes on each side. Serve at once with the sauce.

PER SERVING (2 cakes and 1 tablespoon sauce): 185 Cal, 9 g Fat, 2 g Sat Fat, 0 g Trans Fat, 167 mg Chol, 436 mg Sod, 5 g Carb, 0 g Fib, 19 g Prot, 48 mg Calc. *POINTS* value: *4*.

TRY IT

Panko are light, flaky bread crumbs made from wheat bread. Look for them in Asian grocery stores or the Asian-foods section of the supermarket. If you can't find panko, substitute ¼ cup plain dried bread crumbs.

SCALLOPS WITH LEMONY HUMMUS SAUCE

PREP **10 MIN**   COOK **5 MIN**   SERVES **4**

- **1**   **lemon**
- **¾**   **cup jarred hummus**
- **3**   **tablespoons snipped fresh chives**
- **1**   **pound sea scallops, patted dry**
- **½**   **teaspoon salt**
- **1**   **teaspoon canola oil**
- **1**   **(8-ounce) bag baby spinach**

1 Grate 1¼ teaspoons of the zest from the lemon and set aside; squeeze 2 tablespoons of juice. Combine the hummus, 2 tablespoons of the chives, and the lemon juice in a bowl.

2 Combine the scallops, ½ teaspoon of the lemon zest, and ¼ teaspoon of the salt in a medium bowl. Heat ½ teaspoon of the oil in a large nonstick skillet over medium-high heat. Add half the scallops and cook until golden brown and just opaque in the center, 1–2 minutes on each side. Transfer to a plate. Repeat with the remaining ½ teaspoon oil and the remaining scallops.

3 Add the spinach to the skillet and cook, stirring constantly, just until it begins to wilt. Remove the skillet from the heat; stir in the remaining ¾ teaspoon lemon zest and ¼ teaspoon salt. Divide the spinach and scallops among 4 plates; sprinkle with the remaining 1 tablespoon chives and drizzle with the sauce.

PER SERVING (about 4 scallops with ¾ cup spinach and about ¼ cup sauce): 179 Cal, 6 g Fat, 1 g Sat Fat, 0 g Trans Fat, 30 mg Chol, 658 mg Sod, 13 g Carb, 4 g Fib, 19 g Prot, 168 mg Calc. *POINTS* value: *3*.

SALMON PACKETS WITH OLIVES AND CAPERS

PREP 15 MIN   COOK 15 MIN   SERVES 6

- **1   small fennel bulb, trimmed and thinly sliced**
- **1   small tomato, diced**
- **12 jarred brine-cured kalamata olives, pitted and chopped**
- **2   teaspoons jarred brine-cured capers, drained**
- **2   teaspoons grated lemon zest**
- **2   teaspoons extra-virgin olive oil**
- **6   (4-ounce) skinless salmon fillets**

1 Bring 2 cups of water to a boil in a small saucepan. Add the fennel and cook just until translucent, about 2 minutes. Drain and transfer to a large bowl. Stir in the tomato, olives, capers, lemon zest, and oil; set aside.

2 Meanwhile, preheat the oven to 400°F. Tear off 6 (12x16-inch) sheets of parchment paper. Fold each one in half lengthwise and cut into heart shapes with the fold running vertically down the center. Open each heart flat and spray with olive oil nonstick spray.

3 Place a fillet onto the center of one side of each heart. Top each with about ⅓ cup of the fennel mixture. Fold the parchment over the fennel mixture. Starting at the top of each heart, crimp the edges to seal the packets. Place the on a baking sheet and bake until the fillets are just opaque in the center, 12–15 minutes. Open the packets carefully to let the steam escape. Serve at once, drizzled with any juices.

PER SERVING (1 packet): 200 Cal, 9 g Fat, 2 g Sat Fat, 0 g Trans Fat, 75 mg Chol, 184 mg Sod, 4 g Carb, 2 g Fib, 25 g Prot, 44 mg Calc. *POINTS* value: *4.*

MEATLESS CHILI VERDE

PREP 10 MIN   COOK 15 MIN   SERVES 4

¾ **pound tempeh, diced (about 2 cups)**

3 **garlic cloves, finely chopped**

2 **poblano peppers, coarsely chopped (wear gloves to prevent irritation)**

2 **teaspoons ancho chili powder**

2 **teaspoons ground cumin**

1 **(16-ounce) jar fat-free salsa verde**

¼ **cup fat-free sour cream**

1 Spray a large nonstick skillet with canola oil nonstick spray and set over medium-high heat. Add the tempeh and garlic; cook, stirring occasionally, until the tempeh is lightly browned, about 3 minutes.

2 Stir in the poblanos, chili powder, and cumin; cook, stirring frequently, until the poblanos are crisp-tender, about 2 minutes. Stir in the salsa and ½ cup water; bring to a boil. Reduce the heat and simmer until the poblanos are tender, about 10 minutes.

3 Ladle the chili into 4 bowls and top with the sour cream. Serve at once.

PER SERVING (about 1 cup chili with 1 tablespoon sour cream): 230 Cal, 10 g Fat, 2 g Sat Fat, 0 g Trans Fat, 1 mg Chol, 420 mg Sod, 21 g Carb, 6 g Fib, 18 g Prot, 148 mg Calc. *POINTS* value: **5.**

TRY IT

Tempeh (TEHM-pay) is a fermented soybean cake with a delicious nutty flavor. Look for it in the refrigerated natural-foods section of your supermarket or in natural-foods stores.

BEYOND THE BOX

Hungry and in a hurry? Peek inside the box
and get inspired

GARLICKY PORK AND UDON BOWL

PREP 10 MIN   COOK 20 MIN   SERVES 4

¼	**pound udon**
1	**(32-ounce) carton reduced-sodium chicken broth**
½	**pound bok choy, coarsely chopped**
½	**pound pork tenderloin, trimmed and thinly sliced**
2	**tablespoons reduced-sodium soy sauce**
1	**tablespoon minced peeled fresh ginger**
2	**garlic cloves, finely chopped**

1 Cook the udon according to package directions.

2 Meanwhile, combine the broth, bok choy, pork, soy sauce, ginger, and garlic in a large saucepan; bring just to a simmer over high heat. Reduce the heat and cook until the pork is cooked through and the bok choy is tender, about 10 minutes.

3 Stir in the udon and serve at once.

PER SERVING (1¾ cups): 200 Cal, 3 g Fat, 1 g Sat Fat, 0 g Trans Fat, 36 mg Chol, 947 mg Sod, 24 g Carb, 3 g Fib, 21 g Prot, 96 mg Calc. *POINTS* value: *4*.

MAKE IT CORE

If you want to enjoy this soup on the **Core Plan**, substitute an equal amount of whole-wheat linguine or spaghetti for the Japanese udon noodles (you'll also decrease the per-serving **POINTS** value by **1**).

GARLICKY PORK AND
UDON BOWL

CREOLE RICE AND BEEF

PREP 10 MIN   COOK 20 MIN   SERVES 4

- ¾ **pound boneless sirloin steak, trimmed and cut into ¾-inch cubes**
- ¾ **teaspoon Creole seasoning**
- 1 **onion, diced**
- 1 **green bell pepper, diced**
- 1¾ **cups reduced-sodium chicken broth**
- 1 **(14-ounce) box instant brown rice**
- 1 **(14½-ounce) can stewed tomatoes**

1 Sprinkle the steak with ½ teaspoon of the Creole seasoning. Spray a nonstick Dutch oven with canola oil nonstick spray and set over medium-high heat. Add the steak and cook, stirring frequently, until browned, about 3 minutes. Transfer to a plate.

2 Add the onion, pepper, ¼ cup of the broth, and the remaining ¼ teaspoon Creole seasoning to the Dutch oven. Reduce the heat and simmer, covered, stirring occasionally, until the liquid is absorbed and the vegetables are tender, about 8 minutes.

3 Stir in the rice, tomatoes, and the remaining 1½ cups broth; bring to a boil. Return the steak to the Dutch oven. Reduce the heat and simmer, covered, until the liquid has evaporated, the rice is tender, and the steak is cooked through, about 5 minutes longer. Remove the Dutch oven from the heat; let the mixture stand 5 minutes. Fluff with a fork.

PER SERVING (about 1 cup): 340 Cal, 5 g Fat, 1 g Sat Fat, 0 g Trans Fat, 48 mg Chol, 733 mg Sod, 46 g Carb, 7 g Fib, 27 g Prot, 65 mg Calc. *POINTS* value: **6.**

SPANISH RICE AND CHICKEN BURRITOS

PREP 5 MIN   COOK 10 MIN   SERVES 4

¾ **pound chicken cutlets, cut into ½-inch strips**

1 **(8.8-ounce) package cooked Spanish-style rice**

4 **(8-inch) fat-free flour tortillas**

½ **cup salsa**

¼ **cup shredded reduced-fat pepperjack cheese**

1 Spray a large nonstick skillet with nonstick spray and set over medium-high heat. Add the chicken and cook, turning occasionally, until browned, about 6 minutes. Add the rice and cook, stirring occasionally, until heated through, about 2 minutes.

2 Meanwhile, warm the tortillas according to package directions.

3 Put 1 tortilla on a work surface and spoon 1 cup of the chicken mixture down the center. Top with 2 tablespoons of the salsa and 1 tablespoon of the cheese. Fold the unfilled sides of the tortilla over the filling; then roll up to enclose the filling. Repeat with the remaining tortillas, chicken mixture, salsa, and cheese.

PER SERVING (1 burrito): 282 Cal, 6 g Fat, 2 g Sat Fat, 0 g Trans Fat, 56 mg Chol, 723 mg Sod, 34 g Carb, 4 g Fib, 26 g Prot, 162 mg Calc. *POINTS* value: *5.*

FOOD NOTE

If you prefer your Tex-Mex fare on the mild side, opt for mild salsa and substitute shredded reduced-fat Mexican cheese blend for the pepperjack cheese.

MOROCCAN COUSCOUS WITH CHICKEN AND APRICOTS

PREP 10 MIN   COOK 15 MIN   SERVES 4

1   **pound chicken tenders**

2   **tablespoons mango chutney**

1   **teaspoon Dijon mustard**

1   **(7-ounce) box couscous with nuts, currants, and spices**

6   **dried apricots, cut into thin strips**

2   **tablespoons chopped fresh cilantro**

1 Combine the chicken, chutney, and mustard in a large bowl; toss well to coat. Spray a large nonstick ridged grill pan or skillet with nonstick spray and set over medium-high heat. Add the chicken mixture and cook, turning frequently, until the chicken is cooked through, 6–8 minutes.

2 Meanwhile, prepare the couscous according to package directions.

3 Fluff the couscous with a fork and transfer to a large platter. Top with the chicken mixture, apricots, and cilantro. Serve at once.

PER SERVING (1¼ cups): 342 Cal, 5 g Fat, 1 g Sat Fat, 0 g Trans Fat, 68 mg Chol, 523 mg Sod, 41 g Carb, 3 g Fib, 31 g Prot, 38 mg Calc. *POINTS* value: **7.**

FOOD NOTE

If chutney isn't handy in your pantry, substitute an equal amount of all-fruit apricot or peach spread.

GNOCCHI WITH TURKEY-PORCINI BOLOGNESE

PREP 10 MIN   COOK 15 MIN   SERVES 4

1 (17.6-ounce) package fresh gnocchi

½ ounce dried porcini mushrooms

2 teaspoons olive oil

½ pound ground skinless turkey breast

1 (15½-ounce) jar marinara sauce

¼ cup chopped fresh basil

1. Cook the gnocchi according to package directions, omitting the salt if desired.

2. Meanwhile, place the mushrooms in a small bowl. Pour 1 cup boiling water over them; let stand 5 minutes to soften. With a slotted spoon, remove the mushrooms from the liquid; rinse thoroughly and chop coarsely. Discard the liquid.

3. Heat the oil in a medium nonstick saucepan over medium-high heat. Add the mushrooms and turkey. Cook until the turkey is browned, about 3 minutes, breaking up the turkey with a wooden spoon. Stir in the marinara sauce and bring to a simmer. Remove the saucepan from the heat. Stir in the gnocchi and basil and serve at once.

PER SERVING (1½ cups): 392 Cal, 7 g Fat, 1 g Sat Fat, 0 g Trans Fat, 38 mg Chol, 993 mg Sod, 66 g Carb, 4 g Fib, 19 g Prot, 38 mg Calc. **POINTS** value: **8.**

ZAP IT

To prep dried porcini in a snap, combine the mushrooms and 1 cup water in a small microwavable bowl. Microwave on High until the water comes to a boil, 1–2 minutes. Proceed with the recipe as directed in step 1, skipping step 2.

ISRAELI COUSCOUS SALAD
WITH LAMB

ISRAELI COUSCOUS SALAD WITH LAMB

PREP 10 MIN   COOK 20 MIN   SERVES 4

1   cup Israeli couscous

1   small cucumber, peeled,
    seeded, and diced

3   tablespoons chopped fresh
    mint

2   teaspoons olive oil

1   teaspoon Italian seasoning

1   pound boneless leg of lamb,
    trimmed and cut into 1½-inch
    pieces

1 Bring 2 cups water to a boil in a medium saucepan. Add the couscous. Reduce the heat and simmer, covered, until the couscous is tender, about 10 minutes; drain. Rinse under cold running water; drain and transfer to a bowl. Add the cucumber, mint, oil, and ½ teaspoon of the Italian seasoning; toss well.

2 Meanwhile, spray a broiler rack with nonstick spray and preheat the broiler.

3 Thread the lamb onto 4 (10-inch) metal skewers. Sprinkle the kebabs with the remaining ½ teaspoon Italian seasoning and spray with nonstick spray. Place on the broiler rack and broil 5 inches from the heat until done to taste, about 3 minutes on each side for medium rare. Serve with the salad.

PER SERVING (1 kebab with generous ¾ cup salad): 315 Cal, 11 g Fat, 3 g Sat Fat, 0 g Trans Fat, 78 mg Chol, 67 mg Sod, 24 g Carb, 2 g Fib, 28 g Prot, 27 mg Calc. *POINTS* value: *7.*

TRY IT

Israeli couscous consists of large pearls of toasted pasta that resemble the granules of tapioca or pearl barley. Look for it in larger supermarkets or specialty-foods stores.

MEDITERRANEAN BARLEY AND TUNA SALAD

PREP 10 MIN   COOK 15 MIN   SERVES 4

2   cups reduced-sodium chicken broth or 2 (8-ounce) bottles clam juice

1   cup quick-cooking barley

1   large lemon

1   tomato, diced

½   cup chopped fresh basil

10   pitted kalamata olives, chopped

1   (6-ounce) can chunk light tuna in olive oil, drained well

1 Bring the broth to a boil in a medium saucepan. Add the barley. Reduce the heat and simmer, covered, until the barley is tender, about 10 minutes.

2 Meanwhile, grate 1 tablespoon of the zest from the lemon; squeeze 3 tablespoons of juice. When the barley is done, drain it. Rinse under cold running water; drain again and transfer to a large bowl.

3 Add the tomato, basil, olives, lemon zest, and lemon juice to the barley; toss well to combine. Gently stir in the tuna and serve at once.

PER SERVING (1¼ cups): 279 Cal, 5 g Fat, 1 g Sat Fat, 0 g Trans Fat, 7 mg Chol, 504 mg Sod, 42 g Carb, 9 g Fib, 18 g Prot, 52 mg Calc. *POINTS* value: **5.**

FOOD NOTE

If fresh basil is not available at your market, substitute an equal amount of chopped fresh flat-leaf parsley or dill.

CRAB FRIED RICE

PREP 5 MIN   COOK 15 MIN   SERVES 4

1¾ cups reduced-sodium chicken broth or bottled clam juice

1 (14-ounce) box instant brown rice

4 large eggs

2 tablespoons reduced-sodium soy sauce

¼ pound fresh snow peas, trimmed and cut lengthwise into ¼-inch strips

1 red bell pepper, diced

1 (6-ounce) can cooked lump crabmeat

1 Bring the broth to a boil in a medium saucepan. Stir in the rice and return to a boil. Reduce the heat and simmer, covered, until the rice is tender, about 5 minutes. Remove the saucepan from the heat; let the rice stand, covered, until the liquid is absorbed, about 5 minutes. Spread the rice on a baking sheet and let cool slightly, about 10 minutes.

2 Meanwhile, combine the eggs and soy sauce in a bowl, beating with a whisk until blended.

3 Spray a large nonstick skillet with canola oil nonstick spray and set over medium-high heat. Add the snow peas and bell pepper; cook, stirring frequently, until the vegetables are crisp-tender, about 5 minutes. Add the egg mixture and cook, stirring constantly, until the eggs begin to set, about 1 minute. Add the rice and crabmeat; cook, stirring gently, until heated through, about 2 minutes longer.

PER SERVING (about 1 cup): 330 Cal, 7 g Fat, 2 g Sat Fat, 0 g Trans Fat, 250 mg Chol, 721 mg Sod, 43 g Carb, 7 g Fib, 22 g Prot, 107 mg Calc. *POINTS* value: *6.*

SPICY RED LENTIL STEW

PREP **10 MIN**   COOK **20 MIN**   SERVES **4**

2   **(14½-ounce) cans reduced-sodium chicken broth**

1   **cup red lentils, picked over, rinsed, and drained**

1   **onion, chopped**

1   **carrot, diced**

¾   **teaspoon curry powder**

½   **teaspoon ground cumin**

¾   **pound Swiss chard, stems removed and leaves chopped**

1 Combine the broth, lentils, onion, carrot, curry powder, and cumin in a large saucepan; bring to a boil. Reduce the heat and simmer, covered, until the lentils are tender but still hold their shape, about 15 minutes.

2 Stir in the chard and cook until the lentils and chard are tender, about 5 minutes longer.

PER SERVING (generous 1 cup): 203 Cal, 1 g Fat, 0 g Sat Fat, 0 g Trans Fat, 0 mg Chol, 656 mg Sod, 35 g Carb, 10 g Fib, 17 g Prot, 97 mg Calc. *POINTS* value: **3.**

FOOD NOTE

Red lentils are smaller than the typical brown lentil, and they cook faster too. Look for them in large supermarkets or Middle Eastern or Indian grocery stores.

POLENTA AND SPINACH GRATIN

PREP 5 MIN   COOK 25 MIN   SERVES 4

1 (32-ounce) carton reduced-sodium chicken broth

1 cup instant polenta

1 **cup part-skim ricotta cheese**

1 **large egg**

1 **(9-ounce) bag baby spinach**

2 **garlic cloves, minced**

½ **cup shredded reduced-fat Italian cheese blend**

1 Preheat the oven to 425°F. Spray a 7x11-inch baking dish with nonstick spray.

2 Bring the broth to a boil in a medium saucepan. Slowly pour in the polenta in a thin, steady stream, beating constantly with a whisk. Reduce the heat and cook, continuing to beat with a whisk, until thick and creamy, 3–4 minutes. Remove from the heat. Add the ricotta and egg, beating constantly with a whisk. Spoon mixture into the baking dish.

3 Spray a large nonstick skillet with nonstick spray and set over medium-high heat. Add the spinach and garlic. Cook, stirring constantly, until the spinach begins to wilt, about 3 minutes. Spoon the spinach evenly over the polenta mixture; sprinkle with the cheese blend. Bake until the cheese blend is melted, about 15 minutes.

PER SERVING (1½ cups): 257 Cal, 9 g Fat, 5 g Sat Fat, 0 g Trans Fat, 80 mg Chol, 1,185 mg Sod, 27 g Carb, 3 g Fib, 19 g Prot, 433 mg Calc. *POINTS* value: **5**.

RISOTTO PRIMAVERA

PREP 10 MIN   COOK 20 MIN   SERVES 4

2   teaspoons olive oil

1   zucchini, diced

1   red bell pepper, diced

1   (5.8-ounce) box Arborio rice mix with Parmesan cheese

1   (14½-ounce) can reduced-sodium vegetable broth

1½   cups frozen edamame (green soybeans), thawed

¼   cup chopped fresh basil

1 Heat the oil in a medium nonstick saucepan over medium-high heat. Add the zucchini and pepper; cook, stirring frequently, until the vegetables are tender, about 2 minutes. Add the rice mix and cook, stirring constantly, until the rice begins to appear translucent, about 2 minutes.

2 Stir in the broth and bring to a boil. Reduce the heat and simmer, covered, until the rice is tender, about 15 minutes. Stir in the edamame and cook, covered, until heated through, about 1 minute longer. Stir in the basil and serve at once.

PER SERVING (about 1 cup): 168 Cal, 6 g Fat, 1 g Sat Fat, 0 g Trans Fat, 0 mg Chol, 290 mg Sod, 21 g Carb, 4 g Fib, 9 g Prot, 98 mg Calc. *POINTS* value: **3.**

TRY IT

Arborio (ahr-BAWR-ee-oh) is a short-grain rice from Italy that is used to make the classic dish risotto. It has a higher starch content than long-grain rice and it becomes wonderfully creamy when cooked, so there's no need to use excess fat to produce a great-tasting rice dish.

THAI RAVIOLI

PREP **5 MIN**   COOK **10 MIN**   SERVES **4**

2   **(9-ounce) packages refrigerated reduced-fat cheese ravioli**

1   **red bell pepper, thinly sliced**

2   **teaspoons grated peeled fresh ginger**

½   **teaspoon Thai red curry paste**

1¼ **cups light (reduced-fat) coconut milk**

3   **tablespoons chopped fresh cilantro**

1 Cook the ravioli according to package directions, omitting the salt if desired.

2 Meanwhile, spray a large nonstick skillet with nonstick spray and set over medium-high heat. Add the bell pepper and cook, stirring frequently, until softened, about 3 minutes. Add the ginger and curry paste; cook, stirring constantly, just until fragrant, about 10 seconds. Add the coconut milk and bring just to a simmer.

3 Add the ravioli to the skillet and cook, stirring occasionally, until hot, about 1 minute. Remove the skillet from the heat; stir in the cilantro and serve at once.

PER SERVING (1⅓ cups): 379 Cal, 10 g Fat, 5 g Sat Fat, 0 g Trans Fat, 56 mg Chol, 595 mg Sod, 57 g Carb, 3 g Fib, 18 g Prot, 129 mg Calc. *POINTS* value: **8.**

FOOD NOTE

If you don't have Thai curry paste in your pantry, substitute ¼ teaspoon crushed red pepper.

FETTUCCINE WITH EGGPLANT, MOZZARELLA, AND TOMATOES

PREP **10 MIN**   COOK **20 MIN**   SERVES **6**

½ **pound whole-wheat fettuccine**

¾ **pound eggplant, cut into 1½-inch cubes**

¼ **pound fat-free mozzarella cheese, diced**

½ **cup chopped fresh basil**

10 **sun-dried tomato halves (not packed in oil), coarsely chopped**

2 **tablespoons balsamic vinegar**

2 **teaspoons extra-virgin olive oil**

1 Cook the fettuccine according to package directions, omitting the salt if desired.

2 Meanwhile, spray a large nonstick skillet with olive oil nonstick spray and set over medium-high heat. Add the eggplant, spray with olive oil nonstick spray, and cook, turning frequently, until tender, about 6 minutes.

3 Transfer the eggplant to a large bowl. Add the fettuccine and the remaining ingredients; toss to coat. Serve at once.

PER SERVING (1 cup): 219 Cal, 3 g Fat, 1 g Sat Fat, 0 g Trans Fat, 3 mg Chol, 428 mg Sod, 38 g Carb, 5 g Fib, 12 g Prot, 197 mg Calc. *POINTS* value: **4**.

FOOD NOTE

This dish is also tasty if you substitute ½ cup fat-free ricotta cheese for the mozzarella (the **POINTS** value will remain the same).

KASHA VARNISHKES WITH
CARAMELIZED LEEKS

KASHA VARNISHKES WITH CARAMELIZED LEEKS

PREP 10 MIN   COOK 20 MIN   SERVES 4 (AS A SIDE DISH)

¼   **pound whole-wheat farfalle (bow ties)**

2   **teaspoons olive oil**

2   **leeks, cleaned and thinly sliced (white and light green parts only)**

½   **cup kasha**

1   **large egg**

1½ **cups vegetable broth**

1 Cook the farfalle according to package directions, omitting the salt if desired.

2 Meanwhile, heat 1 teaspoon of the oil in a large nonstick skillet over medium heat. Add the leeks and cook, stirring, until they are golden, about 3 minutes. Transfer to a bowl.

3 Combine the kasha and egg in a small bowl, stirring with a fork until the kasha is well coated. Heat the remaining 1 teaspoon oil in the skillet over medium-high heat. Add the kasha mixture and cook, stirring frequently, until the grains separate, about 5 minutes. Stir in the broth and bring to a boil. Reduce the heat and simmer, covered, until the kasha is tender and the liquid is absorbed, about 8 minutes. Stir in the farfalle and leeks.

PER SERVING (1 cup): 214 Cal, 5 g Fat, 1 g Sat Fat, 0 g Trans Fat, 53 mg Chol, 501 mg Sod, 38 g Carb, 4 g Fib, 8 g Prot, 50 mg Calc. *POINTS* value: *4*.

GOOD IDEA

Serve this dish with roast chicken. Three (1-ounce) slices of cooked skinless, boneless chicken breast for each serving will increase the **POINTS** value by **3**.

SPEEDY FALAFEL SANDWICHES

HANDS-ON PREP 10 MIN   **COOK** 5 MIN   **SERVES** 4

1   cup falafel

4   (6-inch) whole-wheat pitas

1   cup baby arugula

12 grape or cherry tomatoes, halved

¼   cup fat-free ranch dressing

1 Spray a broiler rack with nonstick spray and preheat the broiler.

2 Combine the falafel and ¾ cup water in a medium bowl. Let stand until the water is absorbed, 2–3 minutes. Form the mixture into 12 (1-inch) balls and place on the broiler rack 1 inch apart. Flatten the balls into 1½-inch patties and spray with nonstick spray. Broil 4 inches from the heat until golden brown, about 2 minutes on each side.

3 Cut a pocket in each pita. Fill each pocket with ¼ cup of the arugula, 3 of the patties, and one quarter of the tomatoes. Drizzle the filling evenly with dressing and serve at once.

PER SERVING (1 sandwich): 324 Cal, 6 g Fat, 1 g Sat Fat, 0 g Trans Fat, 1 mg Chol, 661 mg Sod, 57 g Carb, 11 g Fib, 13 g Prot, 70 mg Calc. *POINTS* value: **6.**

GOOD IDEA

For a *POINTS* value–free accompaniment for these sandwiches, pick up a supply of precut carrot and celery sticks from the supermarket salad bar.

EASY VEGETABLE GUMBO

PREP 5 MIN   COOK 25 MIN   SERVES 4

- 1 (15-ounce) can black beans, rinsed and drained
- 1 (14½-ounce) can diced tomatoes with green chiles
- 1 (10-ounce) package frozen cut okra, thawed
- 1 red bell pepper, diced
- 2 cups vegetable broth
- 1 (7-ounce) box seasoned rice mix with nuts

1 Combine the beans, tomatoes, okra, bell pepper, and broth in a large saucepan; bring to a boil. Reduce the heat and simmer, covered, 3 minutes.

2 Stir in the rice mix and simmer, covered, until the rice is tender, about 20 minutes.

PER SERVING (about 1½ cups): 333 Cal, 3 g Fat, 1 g Sat Fat, 0 g Trans Fat, 1 mg Chol, 1,286 mg Sod, 65 g Carb, 12 g Fib, 14 g Prot, 169 mg Calc. *POINTS* value: **6**.

FOOD NOTE

This dish is equally tasty prepared with a 7-ounce box of seasoned rice mix with lentils or Spanish seasoned rice mix.

CRANBERRY-APPLE QUINOA SALAD

PREP 10 MIN   COOK 15 MIN   SERVES 4 (AS A SIDE DISH)

1   cup quinoa, rinsed

2   cups reduced-sodium chicken broth

1   Granny Smith apple, diced

¼   cup dried cranberries

3   scallions, chopped

3   tablespoons fat-free citrus vinaigrette dressing

2   tablespoons toasted walnuts, chopped

1 Combine the quinoa and broth in a medium saucepan; bring to a boil. Reduce the heat and simmer, covered, until the quinoa is tender, about 10 minutes. Drain.

2 Transfer to a large bowl and let cool slightly, about 10 minutes.

3 Add the apple, cranberries, scallions, and dressing to the quinoa; toss to coat. Sprinkle with the walnuts and serve at once.

PER SERVING (1¼ cups): 239 Cal, 5 g Fat, 0 g Sat Fat, 0 g Trans Fat, 0 mg Chol, 408 mg Sod, 44 g Carb, 5 g Fib, 8 g Prot, 51 mg Calc. *POINTS* value: *4.*

FOOD NOTE

Substitute an Asian Pear for the apple and dried cherries for the cranberries, if desired. The **POINTS** value will remain the same.

CRANBERRY-APPLE
QUINOA SALAD

6

FROZEN ASSETS

See how the freezer is an express lane
cook's best friend

STEAK WITH VEGETABLE HASH BROWNS

PREP 5 MIN   COOK 20 MIN   SERVES 4

4   slices turkey bacon, chopped

1   (10-ounce) package frozen baby Brussels sprouts

3   cups frozen hash browns

¼   teaspoon salt

⅛   teaspoon black pepper

4   (3-ounce) filets mignons, about ¾ inch thick, trimmed

2   teaspoons steak seasoning

1 To make the hash, spray a large nonstick skillet with nonstick spray and set over medium-high heat. Add the bacon and cook, stirring occasionally, until it begins to brown, 4–5 minutes. Add the Brussels sprouts and cook, stirring frequently, until they begin to brown, 5–6 minutes. Add the potatoes, salt, and pepper; cook, stirring occasionally, until the Brussels sprouts are tender and the potatoes are lightly browned, 8–9 minutes.

2 Meanwhile, spray a broiler rack with nonstick spray and preheat the broiler.

3 Sprinkle the filets with the steak seasoning and place them on the broiler rack. Broil 5 inches from the heat until an instant-read thermometer inserted into the side of each filet registers 145°F for medium, 4–5 minutes on each side. Serve at once with the hash.

PER SERVING (1 filet with ¾ cup hash): 297 Cal, 10 g Fat, 3 g Sat Fat, 0 g Trans Fat, 51 mg Chol, 860 mg Sod, 25 g Carb, 4 g Fib, 28 g Prot, 29 mg Calc. *POINTS* value: **6.**

STEAK WITH VEGETABLE
HASH BROWNS

BEEF AND BLACK BEAN CHILI

PREP 10 MIN   COOK 20 MIN   SERVES 4

¾ **pound ground lean beef (7% fat or less)**

3 **garlic cloves, minced**

2 **teaspoons chili powder**

1 **(16-ounce) bag frozen mixed Latino-style vegetables with black beans**

1 **(14½-ounce) can diced tomatoes with jalapeño peppers**

½ **teaspoon salt**

1 Heat a large nonstick saucepan over medium-high heat. Add the beef and cook until no longer pink, about 4 minutes, stirring with a wooden spoon to break it up. Add the garlic and chili powder; cook, stirring constantly, until fragrant, about 1 minute. Add the vegetables and cook, stirring occasionally, until the vegetables are thawed, 2–3 minutes.

2 Stir in the tomatoes and bring to a boil. Reduce the heat and simmer, covered, until the chili is slightly thickened, 12–15 minutes. Stir in the salt and serve at once.

PER SERVING (1 cup): 188 Cal, 6 g Fat, 2 g Sat Fat, 0 g Trans Fat, 48 mg Chol, 566 mg Sod, 15 g Carb, 4 g Fib, 20 g Prot, 69 mg Calc. *POINTS* value: *3*.

GOOD IDEA

Top each serving of chili with a colorful combo of 2 tablespoons each of fat-free sour cream, fat-free cheddar cheese, and salsa, if you like; the **POINTS** value will increase by *1*.

CRISPY CAJUN POTATOES WITH HAM

PREP 5 MIN   COOK 15 MIN   SERVES 4

1	tablespoon olive oil
1	pound fully cooked lean boneless reduced-sodium ham steak, cut into ½-inch cubes
3	garlic cloves, minced
3	cups frozen O'Brien potatoes
¼	teaspoon Cajun seasoning

1 Heat the oil in a large nonstick skillet over medium-high heat. Add the ham and cook, stirring occasionally, until lightly browned, 4–5 minutes. Add the garlic and cook, stirring frequently, until lightly browned, about 1 minute.

2 Add the potatoes and Cajun seasoning; cook, stirring frequently, until the potatoes are browned and tender, 7–9 minutes. Serve at once.

PER SERVING (¾ cup): 247 Cal, 9 g Fat, 2 g Sat Fat, 0 g Trans Fat, 54 mg Chol, 1,367 mg Sod, 18 g Carb, 2 g Fib, 23 g Prot, 22 mg Calc. *POINTS* value: *5.*

GOOD IDEA

Scramble some eggs in a nonstick skillet sprayed with nonstick spray to serve with these zesty potatoes (1 large egg with each serving will increase the *POINTS* value by *2*).

PORK WITH STRAWBERRY-RHUBARB COMPOTE

PORK WITH STRAWBERRY-RHUBARB COMPOTE

PREP 15 MIN   COOK 15 MIN   SERVES 4

- 1 (16-ounce) tub frozen sliced strawberries in sugar
- 1½ cups frozen cut rhubarb
- 1 teaspoon minced peeled fresh ginger
- 1 (1-pound) pork tenderloin, trimmed, cut crosswise into 8 pieces, and pounded to about a ½-inch thickness
- ¾ teaspoon ground cumin
- ½ teaspoon salt
- ¼ teaspoon black pepper

1 To make the compote, combine the strawberries, rhubarb, and ginger in a medium saucepan. Cook over medium heat, stirring occasionally, until the rhubarb is tender but still holds its shape and the mixture has thickened slightly, about 15 minutes.

2 Meanwhile, sprinkle the pork with the cumin, salt, and pepper.

3 Spray a ridged grill pan with nonstick spray and set over medium-high heat. Add the pork and cook until an instant-read thermometer inserted into the side of each piece registers 160°F, 6–7 minutes on each side. Serve at once with the compote.

PER SERVING (2 pieces pork with ½ cup compote): 264 Cal, 5 g Fat, 2 g Sat Fat, 0 g Trans Fat, 72 mg Chol, 350 mg Sod, 31 g Carb, 3 g Fib, 27 g Prot, 122 mg Calc. *POINTS* value: **5.**

HOW WE DID IT

To prep the pork easily for quick cooking, we cut the tenderloin into pieces and transferred them, cut side up, to a work surface. Then we flattened each piece with the heel of the hand to an even thickness.

CHICKEN CRÊPES WITH SPINACH AND MUSHROOMS

PREP 10 MIN   COOK 15 MIN   SERVES 4

1 (10-ounce) package frozen chopped spinach

1 (8-ounce) package sliced fresh white mushrooms

⅛ teaspoon salt

⅛ teaspoon black pepper

1 (10-ounce) package sliced cooked chicken breast

4 ounces fat-free cream cheese

4 (7-inch) prepared crêpes

1 Combine the spinach and ¼ cup water in a large nonstick skillet; bring to a boil. Reduce the heat and cook, covered, until thawed and heated through, about 8 minutes. Drain in a sieve and press with the back of a spoon to remove any excess liquid.

2 Spray the skillet with nonstick spray and set over medium-high heat. Add the mushrooms, salt, and pepper; cook, stirring occasionally, until the mushrooms are lightly browned and have released their liquid, 5–6 minutes.

3 Add the spinach and chicken; cook, stirring, until heated through, about 2 minutes. Add the cream cheese and cook, stirring frequently, until melted. Spoon ¾ cup of the filling onto each crêpe and roll up. Serve at once.

PER SERVING (1 crêpe): 289 Cal, 8 g Fat, 3 g Sat Fat, 0 g Trans Fat, 106 mg Chol, 710 mg Sod, 21 g Carb, 3 g Fib, 34 g Prot, 203 mg Calc. *POINTS* value: **6.**

FOOD NOTE

Look for packaged fresh crêpes in the produce section of the supermarket.

CHINESE CHICKEN AND BROCCOLI

PREP 10 MIN   COOK 15 MIN   SERVES 4

4 teaspoons Asian (dark) sesame oil

I pound skinless, boneless chicken breasts, cut into thin strips

I tablespoon minced peeled fresh ginger

I (1-pound) bag frozen broccoli stir-fry mix

I tablespoon black bean sauce with garlic

1 Heat 2 teaspoons of the sesame oil in a large nonstick skillet over medium-high heat. Add the chicken and cook, stirring occasionally, until lightly browned and cooked through, about 5 minutes. Transfer to a plate.

2 Heat the remaining 2 teaspoons sesame oil in the skillet. Add the ginger and cook, stirring constantly, until fragrant, about 30 seconds. Add the broccoli stir-fry mix and cook, stirring occasionally, until the vegetables are crisp-tender, about 5 minutes.

3 Add the chicken and cook, stirring occasionally, until heated through, about I minute. Add the bean sauce and cook, stirring frequently, until well blended, about I minute longer. Serve at once.

PER SERVING (1 cup): 221 Cal, 9 g Fat, 2 g Sat Fat, 0 g Trans Fat, 68 mg Chol, 113 mg Sod, 8 g Carb, 3 g Fib, 28 g Prot, 44 mg Calc. *POINTS* value: **5.**

GOOD IDEA

For grating ginger, use a Microplane-style grater—it makes this task a snap.

EAST-WEST TURKEY TORTILLAS

PREP 10 MIN   COOK 15 MIN   SERVES 4

I   **pound turkey cutlets, cut into thin strips**

I   **(I-pound) bag frozen pepper stir-fry**

I   **tablespoon reduced-sodium soy sauce**

4   **(7-inch) whole-wheat tortillas**

½   **cup mild black bean and corn salsa**

1 Spray a large nonstick skillet with nonstick spray and set over medium-high heat. Add the turkey and cook, stirring occasionally, until lightly browned and cooked through, about 4 minutes. Transfer to a plate.

2 Spray the skillet again with nonstick spray and set over medium-high heat. Add the pepper stir-fry and cook, stirring occasionally, until the vegetables are tender and the liquid has evaporated, 8–9 minutes. Add the turkey and soy sauce; cook, stirring frequently, until the turkey is heated through, about I minute.

3 Meanwhile, warm the tortillas according to package directions. Top each tortilla with I cup turkey mixture and 2 tablespoons salsa. Fold each tortilla in half and serve at once.

PER SERVING (I filled tortilla): 244 Cal, 2 g Fat, I g Sat Fat, 0 g Trans Fat, 75 mg Chol, 486 mg Sod, 25 g Carb, 6 g Fib, 32 g Prot, 46 mg Calc. *POINTS* value: *4.*

ZAP IT

Use the microwave to warm tortillas quickly and easily. Place a stack of tortillas between two slightly dampened paper towels; microwave 20 seconds per tortilla. Keep wrapped until ready to serve. Do not microwave the tortillas in the package: Microwaving might cause the ink on the package to be transferred to the food.

EAST-WEST TURKEY TORTILLAS

BALSAMIC SHRIMP SUCCOTASH

PREP 10 MIN   COOK 20 MIN   SERVES 4

1½ **pounds frozen large peeled and deveined shrimp**

½ **teaspoon salt**

¼ **teaspoon black pepper**

4 **teaspoons olive oil**

1 **onion, diced**

1 **(10-ounce) package frozen mixed vegetables**

2 **teaspoons balsamic vinegar**

1 Place the shrimp in a colander and set under cold running water until thawed, about 5 minutes. Drain well and pat dry with paper towels. Sprinkle the shrimp with ¼ teaspoon of the salt and ⅛ teaspoon of the pepper.

2 Heat 1½ teaspoons of the oil in a large nonstick skillet over medium-high heat. Add half the shrimp and cook just until lightly browned, about 3 minutes on each side. Transfer to a plate. Repeat with another 1½ teaspoons oil and the remaining shrimp.

3 Heat the remaining 1 teaspoon oil in the skillet. Add the onion and cook until crisp-tender, 2–3 minutes. Add the mixed vegetables and cook, stirring occasionally, until tender, 4–5 minutes. Add the vinegar and the remaining ¼ teaspoon salt and ⅛ teaspoon pepper; cook, stirring frequently, until the flavors are blended, about 1 minute. Add the shrimp and cook until heated through.

PER SERVING (about 1¼ cups): 193 Cal, 6 g Fat, 1 g Sat Fat, 0 g Trans Fat, 242 mg Chol, 587 mg Sod, 6 g Carb, 3 g Fib, 28 g Prot, 74 mg Calc. **POINTS** value: **4.**

MEDITERRANEAN SEAFOOD SALAD ☑

PREP 10 MIN   COOK 20 MIN   SERVES 4

1   **(1-pound) bag frozen seafood medley (shrimp, calamari, scallops, shelled mussels, and imitation crabmeat)**

2   **stalks celery, sliced**

1   **small red onion, chopped**

2   **tablespoons lemon juice**

4   **teaspoons extra-virgin olive oil**

¼   **teaspoon salt**

⅛   **teaspoon black pepper**

1 Bring a large pot of water to a boil. Add the mixed seafood and cook just until opaque in the center, 1–2 minutes; drain. Rinse under running cold water until cool; drain and transfer to a large bowl.

2 Add the celery, red onion, lemon juice, oil, salt, and pepper; toss well to coat.

PER SERVING (1 cup): 130 Cal, 6 g Fat, 1 g Sat Fat, 0 g Trans Fat, 141 mg Chol, 291 mg Sod, 4 g Carb, 1 g Fib, 16 g Prot, 56 mg Calc. *POINTS* value: *3*.

GOOD IDEA

Spoon this salad over room-temperature or chilled whole-wheat couscous (⅔ cup cooked whole-wheat couscous for each serving will increase the *POINTS* value by *2*).

SHRIMP, EDAMAME, AND
CARROT SAUTÉ

SHRIMP, EDAMAME, AND CARROT SAUTÉ

PREP 10 MIN   COOK 15 MIN   SERVES 4

1½ cups frozen shelled edamame (green soybeans)

1 pound frozen large peeled and deveined shrimp

½ teaspoon salt

¼ teaspoon black pepper

4 teaspoons olive oil

3 garlic cloves, minced

1½ cups shredded carrot

2 cups cooked barley, optional

1 Cook the edamame according to package directions; drain.

2 Meanwhile, place the shrimp in a colander and set under cold running water until thawed, about 5 minutes. Drain well and pat dry with paper towels. Sprinkle the shrimp with ¼ teaspoon of the salt and ⅛ teaspoon of the pepper. Heat 2 teaspoons of the oil in a large nonstick skillet over medium-high heat. Add the shrimp and cook just until lightly browned and opaque in the center, 2–3 minutes on each side. Transfer to a plate.

3 Heat the remaining 2 teaspoons oil in the skillet. Add the garlic and cook, stirring constantly, just until fragrant, about 15 seconds. Add the edamame and carrots; cook, stirring frequently, until the carrots are crisp-tender, about 2 minutes. Add the shrimp and the remaining ¼ teaspoon salt and ⅛ teaspoon pepper; cook, stirring frequently, just until the shrimp are heated through.

PER SERVING (1 cup without barley): 218 Cal, 9 g Fat, 1 g Sat Fat, 0 g Trans Fat, 161 mg Chol, 517 mg Sod, 11 g Carb, 4 g Fib, 25 g Prot, 129 mg Calc. **POINTS** value: **4.**

CRAB CAKES WITH CHILI-GARLIC MAYONNAISE

PREP 5 MIN   COOK 10 MIN   SERVES 4

⅓   cup fat-free mayonnaise

2   tablespoons chopped fresh cilantro

1   teaspoon chili garlic sauce

2   teaspoons lemon juice

2   (6-ounce) packages frozen crab cakes

2   teaspoons olive oil

1 To make the chili-garlic mayonnaise, combine the mayonnaise, cilantro, chili garlic sauce, and lemon juice in a small bowl. Set aside.

2 Heat the oil in a medium nonstick skillet over medium-high heat. Add the crab cakes and cook, covered, 2 minutes. Turn, reduce the heat, and cook, uncovered, until lightly golden, about 2 minutes. Turn again, press lightly with a spatula to flatten slightly, and cook until lightly golden, 2–3 minutes. Turn and cook until heated through, 2–3 minutes longer. Serve with the chili-garlic mayonnaise.

PER SERVING (1 crab cake with about 1½ tablespoons chili-garlic mayonnaise): 215 Cal, 10 g Fat, 2 g Sat Fat, 1 g Trans Fat, 142 mg Chol, 539 mg Sod, 15 g Carb, 1 g Fib, 15 g Prot, 96 mg Calc. *POINTS* value: **5**.

GOOD IDEA

For an elegant, **POINTS** value–free presentation, serve the crab cakes on a bed of mixed baby lettuce, put the mayonnaise in a small crock, and serve with lemon wedges.

VEGETABLE-CURRY NOODLES

PREP 5 MIN   COOK 20 MIN   SERVES 4

½ **pound rice noodles**

4 **teaspoons canola oil**

1 **(16-ounce) bag frozen mixed Asian vegetables with edamame**

2 **teaspoons curry powder**

1 **(14½-ounce) can reduced-sodium chicken broth**

½ **teaspoon salt**

⅛ **teaspoon black pepper**

1 Cook the rice noodles according to package directions; drain.

2 Meanwhile, heat the oil in a large nonstick skillet over medium-high heat. Add the vegetables and cook until crisp-tender, 7–8 minutes. Add the curry powder and cook, stirring constantly, just until fragrant, about 30 seconds.

3 Add the noodles and cook, stirring constantly, until blended, about 30 seconds. Add the broth, salt, and pepper; cook, stirring frequently, until heated through, about 1 minute longer. Serve at once.

PER SERVING (1½ cups): 324 Cal, 7 g Fat, 1 g Sat Fat, 0 g Trans Fat, 0 mg Chol, 579 mg Sod, 58 g Carb, 5 g Fib, 8 g Prot, 78 mg Calc. *POINTS* value: **6**.

MAKE IT CORE

If you want to enjoy this dish on the **Core Plan,** use ½ pound whole-wheat linguine cooked according to package directions instead of the rice noodles (you'll also reduce the per-serving *POINTS* value by *1*).

EASY PEA SOUP WITH CRAB

PREP 5 MIN   COOK 25 MIN   SERVES 4

2 (14½-ounce) cans reduced-sodium chicken broth

2 cups frozen chopped onions

1 (¾-pound) baking potato, peeled and cubed

1 (16-ounce) bag frozen peas

½ pound frozen cooked lump crabmeat

¼ teaspoon salt

⅛ teaspoon black pepper

1 Combine the broth, onions, and potato in a large saucepan; cover and bring to a boil. Cook, uncovered, until the potatoes are fork-tender, 8–10 minutes. Stir in the peas and bring to a simmer. Reduce the heat and cook until the peas are bright green, about 5 minutes.

2 Remove the saucepan from the heat and let the soup cool 5 minutes. Meanwhile, thaw the crabmeat according to package directions and pick over.

3 Pour the soup into a blender in batches and puree. Return the soup to the saucepan and stir in the salt and pepper. Cook over high heat, stirring, just until heated through, 1–2 minutes. Serve topped with the crabmeat.

PER SERVING (1½ cups with about ¼ cup crabmeat): 246 Cal, 1 g Fat, 0 g Sat Fat, 0 g Trans Fat, 53 mg Chol, 847 mg Sod, 38 g Carb, 7 g Fib, 21 g Prot, 119 mg Calc. **POINTS** value: 4.

PLAN AHEAD

This soup is also wonderful served chilled. Let it cool to room temperature; then refrigerate in an airtight container up to 2 days. Just before serving, stir well and garnish with the crabmeat and a few sliced scallions if you like.

**EASY PEA SOUP
WITH CRAB**

SPINACH PENNE WITH VEGETABLES AND ROMANO

PREP 5 MIN   COOK 20 MIN   SERVES 4

½ **pound spinach penne**

2 **(9-ounce) boxes frozen mixed Tuscan-style vegetables with tomato sauce**

3 **plum tomatoes, chopped**

¼ **cup grated Romano cheese**

1 Cook the penne according to package directions, omitting the salt if desired.

2 Meanwhile, combine the mixed vegetables and ¼ cup + 2 tablespoons water in a large saucepan; cook over medium-high heat just until the water begins to boil. Reduce the heat and simmer, covered, stirring occasionally, until the vegetables are almost thawed, about 5 minutes. Stir in the tomatoes and cook, uncovered, until the tomatoes are softened and the vegetables are heated through, about 5 minutes longer.

3 Combine the penne and the vegetable mixture in a large bowl; toss to coat. Sprinkle with the cheese and serve at once.

PER SERVING (about 1½ cups): 271 Cal, 5 g Fat, 2 g Sat Fat, 0 g Trans Fat, 50 mg Chol, 458 mg Sod, 46 g Carb, 5 g Fib, 11 g Prot, 122 mg Calc. *POINTS* value: **5.**

FOOD NOTE

Try this meatless dish with tricolor pasta—a combination of spinach, tomato, and regular pasta. Fusilli and farfalle, as well as penne, come in tricolor varieties.

VEGETABLE-CHEESE FRITTATA

PREP 5 MIN   COOK 20 MIN   SERVES 4

1   tablespoon extra-virgin
     olive oil

2   garlic cloves, minced

1   (14-ounce) bag frozen cracked
     pepper–seasoned mixed
     vegetables (squash, onion,
     and red bell pepper)

1   (16-ounce) container egg
     substitute

2   tablespoons chopped fresh
     basil or parsley

1   cup shredded reduced-fat
     cheddar cheese

1 Preheat the broiler.

2 Heat the oil in an ovenproof skillet over medium-high heat. Add the garlic and cook, stirring constantly, just until fragrant, about 30 seconds. Add the vegetables and cook, stirring occasionally, until they are tender and most of the liquid has evaporated, about 9 minutes. Add the egg substitute and basil; cook, stirring occasionally, until the egg substitute starts to set, 2–3 minutes. Reduce the heat and cook without stirring until the egg substitute is almost set, about 7 minutes.

3 Place the skillet under the broiler and broil the frittata 5 inches from the heat until the center is set and the top is lightly browned, 1–2 minutes. Cut into 4 wedges.

PER SERVING (1 wedge): 174 Cal, 7 g Fat, 2 g Sat Fat, 0 g Trans Fat, 6 mg Chol, 494 mg Sod, 8 g Carb, 4 g Fib, 21 g Prot, 278 mg Calc. *POINTS* value: *3.*

FOOD NOTE

For a hearty, thick frittata, use a 10-inch ovenproof skillet. If you use a 12-inch skillet, reduce the cooking time in step 2 by 1 to 2 minutes.

SAY "CHEESE"

Delicious recipes that are fast, fresh, and
oh-so-cheesy good

STEAK WITH WINE-AND-HERB CHEESE SAUCE

PREP 10 MIN   COOK 10 MIN   SERVES 4

1 (1-pound) top-round or flank steak, trimmed

½ teaspoon salt

¼ teaspoon black pepper

1 tablespoon olive oil

1 large shallot, minced

¾ cup dry red wine

2 tablespoons reduced-fat garlic-and-herb spreadable cheese

1 Sprinkle the steak with the salt and pepper. Heat a large skillet over medium-high heat. Add the steak and cook until an instant-read thermometer inserted into the side registers 145°F for medium, 3–4 minutes on each side. Transfer to a cutting board; cover loosely with foil and keep warm.

2 To make the sauce, heat the oil in the skillet over medium heat. Add the shallot and cook, stirring occasionally, until it begins to brown, 1–2 minutes. Stir in the wine, increase the heat, and bring to a boil. Cook, scraping up the browned bits from the bottom of the skillet, until the mixture is reduced to ⅓ cup, 3–5 minutes. Remove the skillet from the heat; add the cheese, stirring until melted.

3 Cut the steak into 12 slices; transfer to a platter. Pour the sauce over the steak and serve at once.

PER SERVING (3 slices steak with 1½ tablespoons sauce): 203 Cal, 8 g Fat, 3 g Sat Fat, 0 g Trans Fat, 69 mg Chol, 364 mg Sod, 3 g Carb, 0 g Fib, 27 g Prot, 37 mg Calc. **POINTS** value: **5.**

HAM AND CHEESE BAGUETTES WITH ARUGULA

PREP 10 MIN   COOK 5 MIN   SERVES 4

1 (9-ounce) baguette, ends trimmed

3 tablespoons honey-Dijon mustard

6 ounces thinly sliced fully cooked lean reduced-sodium ham

1 cup shredded reduced-fat Colby and Monterey Jack cheese blend

4 cups baby arugula

1 Preheat the broiler.

2 Cut the baguette crosswise into quarters. Cut each piece in half lengthwise, leaving a ½-inch hinge (do not cut all the way through). Open each piece up like a book. Place the pieces, cut side up, on a broiler rack and broil 3 inches from the heat until lightly toasted, 2–3 minutes.

3 Spread the cut sides of each piece of baguette with the mustard. Layer each bottom half with one quarter of the ham and ¼ cup of the cheese. Broil until the cheese is melted, 2–3 minutes. Top each sandwich with 1 cup of the arugula. Gently press the top halves of the bread over the filling and serve at once.

PER SERVING (1 sandwich): 285 Cal, 9 g Fat, 4 g Sat Fat, 0 g Trans Fat, 35 mg Chol, 1,195 mg Sod, 29 g Carb, 2 g Fib, 21 g Prot, 280 mg Calc. *POINTS* value: *6.*

FOOD NOTE

A crusty French baguette is the perfect choice for these savory sandwiches. To make sure each serving is appropriately hearty, shop for a loaf that's about 20 inches in length.

CHEESY SLOPPY JOES

PREP **5 MIN**   COOK **15 MIN**   SERVES **6**

½ **pound lean ground beef (7% fat or less)**

1 **(10-ounce) package frozen mixed vegetables**

1 **(6-ounce) can tomato paste**

1 **(1.3- or 1.5-ounce) package sloppy joe seasoning mix**

3 **whole-wheat hamburger buns, split**

6 **(¾-ounce) slices fat-free cheddar cheese**

1 Heat a large nonstick skillet over medium-high heat. Add the beef and cook until browned, 4–5 minutes, stirring with a spoon to break it up. Discard any drippings.

2 Stir in the mixed vegetables, 1⅓ cups water, the tomato paste, and seasoning mix; bring to a boil. Reduce the heat and simmer, stirring, until thickened, about 10 minutes.

3 Meanwhile, preheat the broiler. Place the buns, cut side up, on a broiler rack and broil 3 inches from the heat until toasted, 1–2 minutes. Top each bun half with 1 slice of the cheese and broil until the cheese is melted, about 1 minute longer. Spoon ½ cup of the beef mixture on top of each bun half and serve at once.

PER SERVING (1 sloppy joe): 207 Cal, 4 g Fat, 1 g Sat Fat, 0 g Trans Fat, 21 mg Chol, 1,018 mg Sod, 26 g Carb, 5 g Fib, 19 g Prot, 260 mg Calc. *POINTS* value: *4.*

PLAN AHEAD

Make a double batch of the beef mixture and freeze the extra in an airtight container up to 1 month to have on hand for another meal.

CHICKEN AND CHEESE PANINI WITH BALSAMIC MAYONNAISE

PREP 10 MIN   COOK 5 MIN   SERVES 4

2   tablespoons fat-free mayonnaise

2   teaspoons balsamic vinegar

8   slices reduced-calorie multigrain bread

2½ cups sliced cooked chicken breast

16 large fresh basil leaves

1   whole jarred roasted red pepper (not packed in oil), drained and cut into strips

4   (¾-ounce) slices reduced-fat Swiss cheese

1 Combine the mayonnaise and vinegar in a small bowl; spread on 4 slices of the bread. Layer each slice with one quarter of the chicken, 4 basil leaves, one quarter of the roasted peppers, and 1 slice of the cheese. Top with the remaining bread.

2 Spray a ridged grill pan with nonstick spray and set over medium-high heat, or heat a panini sandwich maker according to the manufacturer's instructions. Add the sandwiches (in batches if necessary). Cover with a heavy skillet filled with 1 or 2 soup cans. Grill until the bread is well marked and the cheese is melted, 3–4 minutes on each side. (For the sandwich maker, grill 3–4 minutes.) Serve at once.

PER SERVING (1 sandwich): 296 Cal, 6 g Fat, 2 g Sat Fat, 0 g Trans Fat, 80 mg Chol, 470 mg Sod, 25 g Carb, 7 g Fib, 37 g Prot, 263 mg Calc. *POINTS* value: **6.**

GOOD IDEA

Serve each toasted sandwich with 2 cups assorted carrot, celery, and jicama sticks and 2 tablespoons reduced-fat Italian dressing for dipping (the **POINTS** value will increase by *1*).

TUNA, WHITE BEAN, AND MOZZARELLA SALAD

PREP 10 MIN   COOK NONE   SERVES 4

4   (1-ounce) sticks part-skim
    mozzarella cheese, cut into
    ½-inch pieces

2   (15½-ounce) cans cannellini
    beans, rinsed and drained

2   whole jarred roasted red
    peppers (not packed in oil),
    drained and coarsely chopped

3   tablespoons fat-free Italian
    dressing

2   teaspoons chopped rosemary

1   (6-ounce) can solid white
    tuna in water, drained

2   (6-ounce) romaine hearts, cut
    into ½-inch-thick strips

1 Combine the cheese, beans, roasted peppers, dressing, and rosemary in a large bowl; stir in the tuna.

2 Arrange one quarter of the lettuce on each of 4 plates. Top with the salad and serve at once.

PER SERVING (about 1¼ cups salad with 2 cups lettuce): 356 Cal, 7 g Fat, 4 g Sat Fat, 0 g Trans Fat, 27 mg Chol, 902 mg Sod, 42 g Carb, 11 g Fib, 33 g Prot, 375 mg Calc. *POINTS* value: **7.**

MAKE IT CORE

If you want to enjoy this dish on the **Core Plan,** substitute ¼ pound diced fat-free mozzarella for the cheese sticks (you'll also decrease the **POINTS** value by **1**).

SHRIMP-AND-CHEESE-STUFFED POTATOES

PREP 10 MIN   COOK 10 MIN   SERVES 4

2   (¾-pound) baking potatoes, scrubbed

1   onion, diced

1   green bell pepper, diced

1   (14½-ounce) can diced tomatoes

¾   pound large peeled and deveined shrimp

⅔   cup crumbled fat-free feta cheese

1½ tablespoons chopped fresh oregano

1 Prick the potatoes in several places with a fork; place on a large microwavable plate. Microwave on High until fork-tender, 9–12 minutes, turning once halfway through cooking.

2 Meanwhile, spray a large nonstick skillet with olive oil nonstick spray and set over medium-high heat. Add the onion and bell pepper; cook, stirring, until crisp-tender, 2–3 minutes. Add the tomatoes and shrimp; bring the mixture to a boil. Reduce the heat and simmer, covered, stirring occasionally, until the shrimp are just opaque in the center, 4–6 minutes. Stir in ⅓ cup of the cheese and the oregano.

3 Slice each potato in half lengthwise. Top each half with about 1 cup of the shrimp mixture. Sprinkle with the remaining ⅓ cup cheese and serve at once.

PER SERVING (1 stuffed potato half): 262 Cal, 1 g Fat, 0 g Sat Fat, 0 g Trans Fat, 124 mg Chol, 810 mg Sod, 41 g Carb, 6 g Fib, 22 g Prot, 273 mg Calc. **POINTS** value: **5.**

LINGUINE WITH WINTER SQUASH AND FETA

PREP 10 MIN   COOK 20 MIN   SERVES 4

½   **pound whole-wheat linguine**

2   **(8-ounce) packages peeled cut-up butternut squash**

2   **shallots, thinly sliced**

½   **teaspoon salt**

1   **cup reduced-sodium chicken broth**

1   **(6 ounce) container crumbled fat-free feta cheese**

4   **scallions thinly sliced (white and light green parts only)**

1 Cook the linguine according to package directions, omitting the salt if desired.

2 Meanwhile, spray a large nonstick skillet with olive oil nonstick spray and set over medium-high heat. Add the squash and cook, stirring occasionally, until it begins to brown, about 6 minutes. Add the shallots and salt; cook, stirring occasionally, until the shallots are tender, about 2 minutes. Stir in the broth and bring to a boil. Reduce the heat and simmer, covered, until the squash is fork-tender, about 6 minutes.

3 Combine the linguine, squash mixture, cheese, and scallions in a large bowl; toss well and serve at once.

PER SERVING (about 1½ cups): 324 Cal, 1 g Fat, 1 g Sat Fat, 0 g Trans Fat, 8 mg Chol, 1,185 mg Sod, 59 g Carb, 6 g Fib, 22 g Prot, 462 mg Calc. **POINTS** value: **6.**

FOOD NOTE

If you prefer a meatless meal, just replace the chicken broth with reduced-sodium vegetable broth.

CHEESY BROCCOLI AND CAULIFLOWER SOUP

PREP 15 MIN   COOK 10 MIN   SERVES 6

1½ teaspoons olive oil

1   onion, diced

¼   cup all-purpose flour

1   (32-ounce) carton reduced-sodium vegetable broth

1   (12-ounce) bag fresh broccoli and cauliflower florets, coarsely chopped

1   cup shredded reduced-fat Monterey Jack and cheddar cheese blend

1 Heat the oil in a large saucepan over medium heat. Add the onion and cook, stirring occasionally, until tender, about 5 minutes. Add the flour and cook, stirring constantly, until well blended and cooked through, about 1 minute. Gradually add the broth, stirring constantly, until blended. Add the broccoli and cauliflower; cover and bring to a boil. Reduce the heat and simmer, uncovered, stirring occasionally, until the broccoli and cauliflower are tender, 4–5 minutes. Let the soup cool about 5 minutes.

2 Pour the soup into a blender in batches and puree. Return to the pan; add the cheese, stirring until melted. Serve at once.

PER SERVING (1 cup): 110 Cal, 5 g Fat, 2 g Sat Fat, 0 g Trans Fat, 9 mg Chol, 334 mg Sod, 12 g Carb, 2 g Fib, 6 g Prot, 143 mg Calc. *POINTS* value: **2.**

GOOD IDEA

Serve this creamy soup with toasted high-fiber rolls (a 2-ounce roll for each serving will increase the **POINTS** value by **1**).

SPINACH SALAD WITH CHEESE AND NUT WEDGES

PREP 15 MIN   COOK 5 MIN   SERVES 4

- 1 (15-ounce) can diced beets, drained
- 1½ tablespoons lemon juice
- 4 teaspoons extra-virgin olive oil
- 1 (5-ounce) bag baby spinach
- 3 tablespoons finely chopped shelled pistachios
- 1 (8¾-ounce) package reduced-fat spreadable Swiss cheese wedges (8 wedges)

1 Combine the beets, lemon juice, and oil in a large bowl. Add the spinach and toss to coat. Divide the salad among 4 plates and set aside.

2 Spread the nuts on a sheet of wax paper. Working with one cheese wedge at a time, gently press the nuts onto the 2 long sides.

3 Set a large nonstick skillet over medium heat. Add the cheese wedges, each with one of its nut sides down, and cook until the nuts are browned, about 2 minutes on each side. Divide the cheese wedges among the salads and serve at once.

PER SERVING (2 cheese wedges with 2½ cups salad): 177 Cal, 10 g Fat, 4 g Sat Fat, 0 g Trans Fat, 30 mg Chol, 957 mg Sod, 12 g Carb, 3 g Fib, 12 g Prot, 285 mg Calc. *POINTS* value: 4.

GOOD IDEA

For a heartier salad, toss in 2 cups diced lean ham with the spinach in step 1 (the per-serving *POINTS* value will increase by 2).

NACHO FONDUE

PREP 5 MIN   **COOK** 2 MIN   **SERVES** 8 (AS A SIDE DISH)

1   (16-ounce) can reduced-sodium black beans, rinsed and drained

⅔   cup chunky salsa

½   teaspoon ground cumin

¼   pound reduced-fat pasteurized cheese product, cut into ½-inch pieces (¾ cup)

5   cups reduced-fat tortilla chips

1 Combine the beans, salsa, and cumin in a medium saucepan; bring to a simmer over medium heat. Cook, stirring occasionally, until the mixture is heated through, about 2 minutes. Add the cheese, stirring until melted.

2 Transfer the dip to a fondue pot or bowl; serve warm with the tortilla chips.

PER SERVING (¼ cup dip with about ⅔ cup chips): 148 Cal, 2 g Fat, 1 g Sat Fat, 0 g Trans Fat, 6 mg Chol, 456 mg Sod, 25 g Carb, 5 g Fib, 8 g Prot, 116 mg Calc. *POINTS* value: **2.**

GOOD IDEA

For deluxe-style nachos, sprinkle the dip with ½ pound cooked lean ground beef (7% fat or less) just before serving (the per-serving *POINTS* value will increase by *1*).

NACHO FONDUE

CHEDDAR, CHIVE, AND GARLIC MASHED POTATOES

PREP 10 MIN   COOK 20 MIN   SERVES 4 (AS A SIDE DISH)

1   pound baby white or red potatoes, scrubbed

8   garlic cloves

½   cup reduced-sodium chicken broth

1   cup shredded fat-free cheddar cheese

¼   cup chopped fresh chives

½   teaspoon black pepper

¼   teaspoon salt

1 Combine in a medium saucepan the potatoes, garlic, and enough water to cover by 1 inch; cover and bring to a boil. Reduce the heat and simmer, uncovered, until the potatoes are fork-tender, about 15 minutes.

2 Meanwhile, put the broth in a small microwavable bowl. Microwave on High until hot, 30–60 seconds.

3 Drain the potatoes and garlic. Return to the pan and mash with the broth, cheese, chives, pepper, and salt. Serve at once.

PER SERVING (¾ cup): 150 Cal, 1 g Fat, 0 g Sat Fat, 0 g Trans Fat, 5 mg Chol, 550 mg Sod, 27 g Carb, 3 g Fib, 10 g Prot, 281 mg Calc. **POINTS** value: **2.**

HOW WE DID IT

We left the skins on the potatoes to keep the prep to a minimum. You can mash the spuds with a long-handled fork or potato masher, or an electric mixer.

MOROCCAN PIZZA

PREP 15 MIN   COOK 15 MIN   SERVES 6

1 (13.8-ounce) can refrigerated pizza crust

¾ cup + 2 tablespoons pizza sauce

½ cup crumbled reduced-fat feta cheese

12 kalamata olives, pitted and thinly sliced

2 scallions, thinly sliced

½ teaspoon crushed red pepper

¼ cup fresh mint leaves, torn

1 Preheat the oven to 400°F. Spray a large baking sheet with nonstick spray.

2 Unroll the pizza crust and place on the baking sheet. Press the dough into a 14x10-inch rectangle. Spread the pizza sauce on the dough, leaving a 1-inch border. Sprinkle the sauce evenly with the cheese, olives, scallions, and crushed red pepper.

3 Bake on the bottom rack of the oven until the crust is golden and the cheese has softened, 14–16 minutes. Sprinkle with the mint and serve at once.

PER SERVING (⅙ th of pizza): 243 Cal, 6 g Fat, 1 g Sat Fat, 0 g Trans Fat, 4 mg Chol, 617 mg Sod, 40 g Carb, 2 g Fib, 7 g Prot, 74 mg Calc. *POINTS* value: **5.**

FOOD NOTE

For an Italian-style pizza, substitute ½ cup shredded part-skim mozzarella for the feta cheese, and substitute fresh basil for the mint (the **POINTS** value will remain the same).

WALDORF-STYLE BULGUR
SALAD WITH BLUE CHEESE

WALDORF-STYLE BULGUR SALAD WITH BLUE CHEESE

PREP 10 MIN   **COOK** 5 MIN   **SERVES** 4 (AS A SIDE DISH)

⅔ **cup bulgur**

1 **Fuji or Gala apple, diced**

½ **cup crumbled blue cheese**

2 **stalks celery, diced**

1 **tablespoon sherry vinegar**

4 **fresh flat-leaf parsley sprigs, chopped**

1 Bring 1 cup water to a boil in a small saucepan. Stir in the bulgur; remove the pan from the heat. Cover and let stand until the water is absorbed, about 25 minutes.

2 Fluff the bulgur with a fork. Add the remaining ingredients, stirring just until combined, and serve at once.

PER SERVING (scant 1 cup): 162 Cal, 5 g Fat, 3 g Sat Fat, 0 g Trans Fat, 13 mg Chol, 259 mg Sod, 24 g Carb, 5 g Fib, 7 g Prot, 112 mg Calc. *POINTS* value: *3*.

GOOD IDEA

Serve this crunchy salad with skinless, boneless chicken breasts cooked in a ridged grill pan (a 3-ounce cooked skinless chicken breast for each serving will increase the *POINTS* value by *3*).

SWEET CHEATS

Our luscious desserts only look
time-consuming to make

APRICOT UPSIDE-DOWN CAKES

PREP 10 MIN   COOK 10 MIN   SERVES 6

6   **tablespoons sugar**

1½ **tablespoons lemon juice**

½   **teaspoon apple pie spice**

1   **(16-ounce) can apricot halves in juice, drained**

6   **refrigerated buttermilk biscuits (from a 7½-ounce can)**

1 Preheat the oven to 425°F. Spray a 6-cup muffin pan with nonstick spray.

2 Combine 5 tablespoons of the sugar, the lemon juice, and pie spice and in a small bowl. Spoon the sugar mixture evenly into the cups. Place 3 overlapping apricot halves, cut side up, in each cup. Then add 1 biscuit to each cup, gently pressing it along the side of the cup to adhere. Sprinkle each biscuit with ½ teaspoon of the remaining sugar.

3 Bake until the apricot mixture is bubbly and the biscuits are golden brown, about 12 minutes. Let the cakes stand in the pan 5 minutes. Invert the cakes on a large plate and serve warm.

PER SERVING (1 cake): 173 Cal, 4 g Fat, 1 g Sat Fat, 1 g Trans Fat, 0 mg Chol, 328 mg Sod, 33 g Carb, 1 g Fib, 2 g Prot, 14 mg Calc. **POINTS** value: **4**.

GOOD IDEA

Serve these cakes with 1½ cups frozen vanilla fat-free yogurt (this will increase the per-serving **POINTS** value by **1**).

APRICOT UPSIDE-DOWN CAKES

ANGEL FOOD CAKE WITH CHERRY-BERRY SAUCE

PREP **5 MIN**   COOK **5 MIN**   SERVES **4**

1   cup frozen dry-packed pitted sweet cherries, halved

¼   cup seedless raspberry jam

2   teaspoons balsamic vinegar

2   pinches ground allspice

½   teaspoon lemon juice

4   (2-ounce) slices store-bought angel food cake

1 To make the sauce, combine the cherries, jam, vinegar, and allspice in a small saucepan. Bring to a simmer over medium heat. Reduce the heat and cook until the cherries are heated through and the mixture thickens slightly, about 3 minutes.

2 Transfer the cherry mixture to a small bowl and let stand until slightly cooled, about 10 minutes. Stir in the lemon juice. Serve the warm sauce with the cake.

PER SERVING (1 slice cake with 2 tablespoons sauce): 247 Cal, 0 g Fat, 0 g Sat Fat, 0 g Trans Fat, 0 mg Chol, 432 mg Sod, 57 g Carb, 1 g Fib, 5 g Prot, 15 mg Calc. **POINTS** value: **5.**

FOOD NOTE

If you're looking for an additional garnish for this dessert, top each serving with 1 tablespoon light whipped topping (the **POINTS** value will remain the same).

NO-BAKE CARAMEL-APPLE CRISPS

PREP 10 MIN   COOK 10 MIN   SERVES 4

1½ **pounds cooking apples (such as Empire or Granny Smith), peeled and thinly sliced**

¾ **teaspoon cinnamon**

2 **tablespoons fat-free caramel topping**

½ **cup reduced-fat cluster-crunch cereal**

1 **tablespoon toffee-bar bits**

1 To make the filling, spray a large nonstick skillet with nonstick spray and set over medium heat. Add the apples and cinnamon; cook, covered, stirring occasionally, until the apples are just tender, about 8 minutes. Stir in the caramel topping. Increase the heat and cook, uncovered, stirring occasionally, until the filling thickens, about 2 minutes.

2 Spoon a scant ¾ cup of the filling onto each of 4 serving dishes. Sprinkle each one with 2 tablespoons cereal and ¾ teaspoon toffee bits and serve at once.

PER SERVING (1 crisp) 172 Cal, 3 g Fat, 1 g Sat Fat, 0 g Trans Fat, 5 mg Chol, 73 mg Sod, 39 g Carb, 3 g Fib, 2 g Prot, 25 mg Calc. *POINTS* value: *3*.

PLAN AHEAD

Make the crisps as directed, but divide the filling among 4 microwavable dishes. Cover each with plastic wrap and refrigerate up to 2 days. When ready to serve, microwave one dish at a time, covered, on High until heated through, 45–60 seconds. Then add the toppings as directed.

LEMON MERINGUE TARTLETS

PREP 20 MIN   COOK NONE   MAKES 15

⅓ cup prepared lemon curd

½ teaspoon grated lemon zest

½ cup marshmallow cream

1 (2.1-ounce) package frozen fully baked mini–phyllo shells (15 shells), thawed

1 To make the filling, combine the lemon curd and lemon zest in a small bowl. Add 2 tablespoons of the marshmallow cream, gently folding in with a rubber spatula just until blended.

2 Spoon 1 rounded teaspoon of the filling into each phyllo shell. Top each one with 1 rounded teaspoon of the remaining marshmallow cream.

PER SERVING (1 tartlet): 44 Cal, 0 g Fat, 0 g Sat Fat, 0 g Trans Fat, 5 mg Chol, 20 mg Sod, 9 g Carb, 0 g Fib, 0 g Prot, 1 mg Calc. *POINTS* value: *1*.

PLAN AHEAD

To make these sweets in advance, insert a toothpick into the center of each tartlet to protect the topping, cover loosely with plastic wrap, and refrigerate overnight.

COCONUT-SORBET SANDWICHES

PREP 15 MIN   COOK NONE   SERVES 12

¾ **cup coconut sorbet, softened**

24 **vanilla mini–meringue cookies**

¼ **cup shredded coconut**

1 Place a large plate in the freezer. Spoon
1 tablespoon of the sorbet onto the flat side
of 1 meringue cookie. Place another
meringue, flat side down, on top of the
sorbet and gently press to make a sandwich.
Place the sandwich on the plate in the
freezer. Repeat with the remaining sorbet
and meringues to make a total of
12 sandwiches.

2 Roll the sides of each sandwich in the
coconut to coat the sorbet; return to the
freezer. Serve at once or transfer to an
airtight container and freeze up to 2 weeks.

PER SERVING (1 sandwich): 45 Cal, 1 g Fat, 1 g Sat Fat, 0 g Trans Fat, 0 mg Chol, 6 mg Sod, 8 g Carb,
0 g Fib, 0 g Prot, 2 mg Calc. **POINTS** value: **1**.

GOOD IDEA

When assembling the sandwiches in step 2, use a melon baller to scoop the sorbet.

PEAR-OATMEAL CRISP

PEAR-OATMEAL CRISP

PREP 15 MIN   COOK 20 MIN   SERVES 6

- ½ **cup + 1 tablespoon all-purpose flour**
- 7 **tablespoons packed brown sugar**
- ¾ **teaspoon ground ginger**
- 2 **(16-ounce) cans sliced pears in juice, drained, with ⅓ cup of the juice reserved**
- 2 **tablespoons butter, melted**
- 1 **(1¼-ounce) package cinnamon and spice instant-oatmeal mix**

1 Preheat the oven to 425°F.

2 Mix 1 tablespoon of the flour, 4 tablespoons of the brown sugar, and the ginger in an 8-inch square baking dish. Add the pears and the reserved pear juice, stirring until blended. Cover the dish with plastic wrap; then prick a few holes in the plastic. Microwave on High until the filling begins to bubble, 4–5 minutes, stirring once halfway through cooking.

3 Meanwhile, combine the butter and the remaining 3 tablespoons brown sugar in a bowl. Add the oatmeal mix and the remaining ½ cup flour; stir until crumbly. Sprinkle evenly over the filling. Transfer the dish to the oven and bake until the topping is golden, about 15 minutes. Serve warm.

PER SERVING (½ cup): 225 Cal, 4 g Fat, 3 g Sat Fat, 0 g Trans Fat, 10 mg Chol, 82 mg Sod, 46 g Carb, 3 g Fib, 2 g Prot, 47 mg Calc. *POINTS* value: **4.**

FOOD NOTE

This versatile crisp can also be prepared with canned sliced apples or apricot halves packed in juice.

RICOTTA AND CHERRY SPONGE CAKES

PREP 15 MIN   COOK NONE   SERVES 6

⅔ cup part-skim ricotta cheese

1¼ cups frozen dry-packed pitted sweet cherries

1½ tablespoons seedless raspberry jam

6   (2½-inch) store-bought sponge cake shells

1½ tablespoons confectioners' sugar

2   tablespoons grated bittersweet or semisweet chocolate

1 Line a large plate with a double layer of paper towels. Spread the cheese over the top and cover with another double layer of paper towels, pressing lightly to adhere. Let the cheese drain 10 minutes.

2 Meanwhile, place the cherries in a colander and set under cold running water until thawed, about 3 minutes. Drain well and pat dry with paper towels. Cut cherries in half. Spread ¾ teaspoon of the jam into each cake shell to cover. Top each one with one quarter of the cherries, cut sides down.

3 Transfer the drained cheese to a bowl; stir in the confectioners' sugar and 1 tablespoon of the chocolate. Spoon the cheese mixture evenly onto the cherries. Sprinkle each cake with ½ teaspoon of the remaining chocolate.

PER SERVING (1 cake): 162 Cal, 4 g Fat, 2 g Sat Fat, 0 g Trans Fat, 46 mg Chol, 48 mg Sod, 27 g Carb, 1 g Fib, 5 g Prot, 87 mg Calc. **POINTS** value: **3.**

**RICOTTA AND CHERRY
SPONGE CAKES**

LEMON-CORNMEAL
MADELEINES

LEMON-CORNMEAL MADELEINES

PREP 10 MIN   COOK 10 MIN   SERVES 24

- 1 **lemon**
- 1 **egg white**
- 4 **tablespoons confectioners' sugar**
- 1 **(8½-ounce) package corn-muffin mix (without added butter)**
- 2 **tablespoons butter, melted**

1 Preheat the oven to 375°F. Spray 48 mini–madeleine molds or 2 (12-cup) mini–muffin pans with nonstick spray.

2 Grate 1 teaspoon of the zest from the lemon; squeeze 2 tablespoons of juice. Combine the egg white and 3 tablespoons water in a medium bowl, beating with a whisk until blended. Stir in the lemon zest, lemon juice, and 2 tablespoons of the confectioners' sugar. Add the muffin mix and melted butter; stir just until blended.

3 Spoon the batter into the madeleine molds, filling them two thirds full. Bake until the edges are golden and the tops spring back when lightly pressed in the center, about 8 minutes. Immediately invert the madeleines on racks and let cool. Sprinkle with the remaining 2 tablespoons confectioners' sugar just before serving.

PER SERVING (2 mini-madeleines): 56 Cal, 2 g Fat, 1 g Sat Fat, 0 g Trans Fat, 3 mg Chol, 121 mg Sod, 8 g Carb, 1 g Fib, 1 g Prot, 7 mg Calc. *POINTS* value: *1*.

TROPICAL MINI-SCONES

PREP 15 MIN   COOK 15 MIN   SERVES 12

2   **cups reduced-fat baking mix**

⅓   **cup dried tropical fruit mix, chopped**

2   **tablespoons crystallized ginger, chopped**

¼   **teaspoon apple pie spice**

¼   **cup maple syrup**

1   **egg white**

3   **tablespoons packed brown sugar**

1 Preheat the oven to 425°F. Spray a large baking sheet with nonstick spray.

2 Combine the baking mix, fruit mix, crystallized ginger, and pie spice in a medium bowl; make a well in the center. Add the maple syrup, 3 tablespoons water, the egg white, and 2 tablespoons of the brown sugar to the well; stir to blend the maple syrup mixture. Combine the maple syrup mixture and the dry ingredients to make a soft dough.

3 Divide the dough into 2 mounds and place them on the baking sheet 5 inches apart. Spread each mound into a 5-inch circle. With a floured knife, cut each circle into 6 wedges. Sprinkle the tops with the remaining 1 tablespoon brown sugar. Bake until the scones are browned and a toothpick inserted into the center comes out clean, about 12 minutes. Serve warm.

PER SERVING (1 mini-scone): 118 Cal, 1 g Fat, 0 g Sat Fat, 0 g Trans Fat, 0 mg Chol, 224 mg Sod, 25 g Carb, 1 g Fib, 2 g Prot, 85 mg Calc. *POINTS* value: **2**.

INSTANT CHOCOLATE-HAZELNUT MOUSSE

PREP 10 MIN   COOK NONE   SERVES 4

1½ tablespoons chocolate-hazelnut spread

4   tablespoons chocolate syrup

2¼ cups fat-free whipped topping

1 Combine the chocolate-hazelnut spread and 3 tablespoons of the chocolate syrup in a medium bowl. Add 2 cups of the whipped topping, gently folding it in with a rubber spatula just until blended.

2 Spoon ½ cup of the mousse into each of 4 dessert goblets. Top each one with 1 tablespoon whipped topping and ¾ teaspoon chocolate syrup. Serve at once or cover and refrigerate up to 2 days.

PER SERVING (1 mousse): 149 Cal, 3 g Fat, 1 g Sat Fat, 0 g Trans Fat, 0 mg Chol, 28 mg Sod, 31 g Carb, 1 g Fib, 1 g Prot, 13 mg Calc. *POINTS* value: *3.*

FOOD NOTE

Look for chocolate-hazelnut spread near the jam and peanut butter in your supermarket.

CARAMEL-COFFEE FONDUE

PREP 5 MIN   COOK 1 MIN   SERVES 4

2   tablespoons fat-free half-and-half

½   teaspoon instant-coffee granules

3   tablespoons white-chocolate chips

3   tablespoons fat-free caramel topping

3   cups assorted cut-up fresh fruit (such as apple, pineapple, and strawberries)

1 To make the fondue, place the half-and-half in a small microwavable bowl. Sprinkle with the coffee and let stand until the granules dissolve, about 1 minute. Add the chocolate chips and microwave on High 20–30 seconds, just until the mixture begins to simmer. Stir until smooth. Add the caramel topping and stir until blended.

2 Transfer the fondue to a serving dish. Serve warm with the assorted fruit for dipping.

PER SERVING (1½ tablespoons fondue and ¾ cup assorted fruit): 152 Cal, 3 g Fat, 2 g Sat Fat, 0 g Trans Fat, 2 mg Chol, 73 mg Sod, 33 g Carb, 2 g Fib, 2 g Prot, 52 mg Calc. *POINTS* value: *3.*

PLAN AHEAD

Make a double batch of fondue and transfer the extra to a microwavable airtight container to enjoy later in the week (the fondue can be refrigerated up to 5 days). To reheat, microwave on High 40–50 seconds, stirring once halfway through cooking.

TAPIOCA BERRY PARFAITS

PREP 15 MIN   COOK NONE   SERVES 4

¾ cup light cherry pie filling

2 cups fresh strawberries, hulled and quartered

¾ cup fresh blueberries

½ cup fresh raspberries

1 tablespoon chopped fresh mint + 4 fresh mint sprigs

3 (3½-ounce) containers fat-free tapioca pudding

1 Combine the pie filling, strawberries, blueberries, raspberries, and chopped mint in a large bowl, stirring just until blended.

2 In each of 4 dessert goblets, layer ⅓ cup of the fruit mixture, ¼ cup of the pudding, and the remaining ⅓ cup fruit mixture. Top each serving with 2 tablespoons of the remaining pudding and a mint sprig. Serve at once.

PER SERVING (1 parfait): 168 Cal, 1 g Fat, 0 g Sat Fat, 0 g Trans Fat, 1 mg Chol, 160 mg Sod, 41 g Carb, 4 g Fib, 3 g Prot, 68 mg Calc. *POINTS* value: *3*.

FOOD NOTE

If you're not a fan of tapioca, use vanilla fat-free pudding instead.

TROPICAL FRUIT SOUP

PREP 10 MIN   COOK NONE   SERVES 4

- **1**   **large mango, halved, peeled, and pitted**
- **1**   **(16-ounce) bottle diet tropical-blend juice drink**
- **3**   **tablespoons frozen limeade concentrate**
- **2**   **tablespoons thinly sliced fresh mint + 4 fresh mint sprigs**
- **6**   **ice cubes**
- **2**   **kiwi fruits, peeled and diced**
- **1**   **cup fresh raspberries**

1 Dice half the mango and set aside for the topping.

2 To make the soup, cut the remaining mango half into quarters and transfer to a blender. Add the juice drink, limeade concentrate, sliced mint, and ice cubes, and puree.

3 Pour 1 cup of the soup into each of 4 dessert goblets. Sprinkle evenly with the kiwi fruits, raspberries, and the reserved diced mango. Top each serving with a mint sprig and serve at once.

PER SERVING (1⅓ cups): 109 Cal, 1 g Fat, 0 g Sat Fat, 0 g Trans Fat, 0 mg Chol, 4 mg Sod, 27 g Carb, 4 g Fib, 1 g Prot, 48 mg Calc. *POINTS* value: *1*.

GOOD IDEA

Top each serving of this refreshing dessert soup with a scoop of lemon or raspberry sorbet (a ¼-cup scoop will increase the *POINTS* value by *1*).

TROPICAL FRUIT SOUP

MANGO–PASSION FRUIT WHIP

PREP 10 MIN   COOK NONE   SERVES 4

2 cups chopped frozen passion fruit pulp

1 cup cubed peeled fresh mango

1 (6-ounce) container lemon reduced-fat yogurt

¼ cup honey

5 ice cubes

1 drop coconut extract (optional)

Puree the passion fruit pulp, mango, 1 cup water, the yogurt, honey, ice cubes, and coconut extract (if using) in a blender. Pour the whip into 4 glasses and serve at once.

PER SERVING (1 cup): 225 Cal, 1 g Fat, 0 g Sat Fat, 0 g Trans Fat, 1 mg Chol, 61 mg Sod, 56 g Carb, 13 g Fib, 5 g Prot, 82 mg Calc. *POINTS* value: **4.**

FOOD NOTE

Look for packages of passion fruit pulp with other frozen Hispanic foods at the supermarket (you will need about 8 ounces of pulp for this recipe). This whip is also delicious made with frozen papaya pulp.

WATERMELON FROSTIES

PREP 10 MIN   COOK NONE   SERVES 2

2   **cups seedless watermelon cubes**

1   **cup ice cubes**

½   **cup light cran-raspberry juice**

3   **tablespoons seedless raspberry all-fruit spread**

2   **teaspoons lime juice**

Puree the watermelon, ice cubes, cran-raspberry juice, fruit spread, and lime juice in a blender. Pour the mixture into 2 glasses and serve at once.

PER SERVING (1½ cups): 131 Cal, 0 g Fat, 0 g Sat Fat, 0 g Trans Fat, 0 mg Chol, 8 mg Sod, 33 g Carb, 3 g Fib, 2 g Prot, 25 mg Calc. *POINTS* value: **2.**

FOOD NOTE

To give these frosties a golden blush, substitute an equal amount of cantaloupe for the watermelon. You can also garnish these sweet refreshers with lime wedges.

MOCHA LATTE SHAKES

PREP 10 MIN   COOK NONE   SERVES 2

⅓   **cup fat-free half-and-half**

5   **ice cubes, coarsely crushed**

1½   **tablespoons + ¼ teaspoon instant-cocoa mix**

¾   **cup coffee reduced-fat ice cream**

4   **tablespoons fat-free whipped topping**

1 Puree the half-and-half, ice, and 1½ tablespoons cocoa mix in a blender. Add the ice cream and puree.

2 Pour the mixture into 2 coffee cups. Top each serving with 2 tablespoons whipped topping and ⅛ teaspoon of the remaining cocoa mix.

PER SERVING (about 1 cup): 164 Cal, 5 g Fat, 3 g Sat Fat, 0 g Trans Fat, 16 mg Chol, 113 mg Sod, 29 g Carb, 1 g Fib, 4 g Prot, 120 mg Calc. *POINTS* value: *3.*

FOOD NOTE

If you're not a mocha fan, use chocolate or vanilla reduced-fat ice cream instead of coffee ice cream, and serve the shakes in glasses.

LITE BANANAS FOSTER

PREP 15 MIN   COOK 10 MIN   SERVES 4

4   medium-ripe bananas,
      crosswise in half, then cut
      each piece lengthwise in half

3   teaspoons unsalted butter

3   tablespoons dark rum

¼   cup packed brown sugar

1⅓   cups vanilla fat-free frozen
      yogurt

1 To make the topping, melt 1½ teaspoons of the butter in a large nonstick skillet over medium heat. Add half the bananas, cut-side down, and cook until golden brown, about 1½ minutes on each side. Transfer to a plate and set aside. Repeat with the remaining 1½ teaspoons butter and bananas, but leave the banana mixture in the skillet.

2 Return the reserved bananas to the skillet. Add the rum and brown sugar; cook until sugar dissolves and mixture is syrupy, about 2 minutes.

3 Divide the yogurt into 4 dishes and spoon the topping evenly over each serving. Serve at once.

PER SERVING (⅓ cup frozen yogurt with scant ½ cup topping): 264 Cal, 3 g Fat, 2 g Sat Fat, 0 Trans Fat, 9 mg Chol, 52 mg Sod, 56 g Carb, 3 g Fib, 4 g Prot, 125 mg Calc. *POINTS* value: **5.**

FOOD NOTE

Instead of the rum, substitute an equal amount of apple cider with ½ teaspoon rum or vanilla extract.

RECIPE INDEX

C

S

POINTS VALUE RECIPE INDEX

DRY AND LIQUID MEASUREMENT EQUIVALENTS

If you are converting the recipes in this book to metric measurements, use the following chart as a guide.

TEASPOONS	TABLESPOONS	CUPS	FLUID OUNCES
3 teaspoons	1 tablespoon		½ fluid ounce
6 teaspoons	2 tablespoons	⅛ cup	1 fluid ounce
8 teaspoons	2 tablespoons plus 2 teaspoons	⅙ cup	
12 teaspoons	4 tablespoons	¼ cup	2 fluid ounces
15 teaspoons	5 tablespoons	⅓ cup minus 1 teaspoon	
16 teaspoons	5 tablespoons plus 1 teaspoon	⅓ cup	
18 teaspoons	6 tablespoons	¼ cup plus 2 tablespoons	3 fluid ounces
24 teaspoons	8 tablespoons	½ cup	4 fluid ounces
30 teaspoons	10 tablespoons	½ cup plus 2 tablespoons	5 fluid ounces
32 teaspoons	10 tablespoons plus 2 teaspoons	⅔ cup	
36 teaspoons	12 tablespoons	¾ cup	6 fluid ounces
42 teaspoons	14 tablespoons	1 cup minus 2 tablespoons	7 fluid ounces
45 teaspoons	15 tablespoons	1 cup minus 1 tablespoon	
48 teaspoons	16 tablespoons	1 cup	8 fluid ounces

VOLUME	
¼ teaspoon	1 milliliter
½ teaspoon	2 milliliters
1 teaspoon	5 milliliters
1 tablespoon	15 milliliters
2 tablespoons	30 milliliters
3 tablespoons	45 milliliters
¼ cup	60 milliliters
⅓ cup	80 milliliters
½ cup	120 milliliters
⅔ cup	160 milliliters
¾ cup	175 milliliters
1 cup	240 milliliters
1 quart	950 milliliters

LENGTH	
1 inch	25 millimeters
1 inch	2.5 centimeters

WEIGHT	
1 ounce	30 grams
¼ pound	120 grams
½ pound	240 grams
1 pound	480 grams

OVEN TEMPERATURE			
250°F	120°C	400°F	200°C
275°F	140°C	425°F	220°C
300°F	150°C	450°F	230°C
325°F	160°C	475°F	250°C
350°F	180°C	500°F	260°C
375°F	190°C	525°F	270°C

NOTE: Measurement of less than ⅛ teaspoon is considered a dash or a pinch. Metric volume measurements are approximate.